THE CONQUEST OF SPACE

THE CONQUEST OF SPACE

PAINTINGS BY

CHESLEY BONESTELL

TEXT

WILLY LEY

LONDON 1952

READERS UNION with **SIDGWICK AND JACKSON**

This Readers Union edition was produced in 1952 for sale to its members only, by Readers Union Ltd at 38, William IV St, in the City of Westminster and at Letchworth Garden City, Hertfordshire. This book has been set in 12 point Baskerville type, leaded and printed by Purnell and Sons Ltd, Paulton, Somerset. The first English edition was published by Sidgwick and Jackson Ltd.

CONTENTS

LIST OF FIGURES

LIST OF PAINTINGS

8

INTRODUCTION: MOSTLY ABOUT CHESLEY BONESTELL

CHESLEY BONESTELL's paintings should not be considered "artist's conceptions" in the customary sense of the phrase. Naturally a picture of Saturn as seen from its sixth moon has to be an "artist's conception" in one sense, since we don't yet have spaceships which could bring the artist to Saturn's sixth moon. If we did, there would still be certain difficulties with the actual painting, since the aforementioned artist would either have to paint through the window of the ship, or sit in a space suit at a temperature of approximately minus 150 degrees Fahrenheit and see what his paints would do at that temperature in an atmosphere consisting mostly of methane gas.

But before I explain the special qualities of these paintings and enumerate Chesley Bonestell's special qualifications for the task of painting more than half a hundred astronomical pictures, I want to answer a question that is probably in the minds of most readers. I know from experience with others as well as from my own reaction that everybody who sees a book with the names of two people on the cover wants to know who did what. Most of the time the collaborators aren't so sure themselves afterwards, but in this particular case there was a natural division of labour which makes it easy to answer the question. All the paintings, whether reproduced here in full colour or in black and white, are Bonestell's work, a number of them done after consultation with astronomers of Mount Wilson and Palomar Observatories. The text is mine and so are the drawings in the text. The captions for the paintings are true collaboration—they were written by both of us together.

After the manuscript was finished, Dr. Robert S. Richardson was kind enough to read it and offer advice on a number of specific points. His aid is hereby gratefully acknowledged.

Work on this book began early in 1948, but this does not mean that work on the paintings was begun so recently. Early in 1948 all the paintings in this book, plus about a dozen others which did not get in, were finished. Many of the pictures had been published in magazines, starting with the set of views of Saturn from its various satellites which appeared in *Life*. By the time the first discussions about the book were held, editors who had published Bonestell pictures in the pages or on the covers of their magazines were already hardened to letters from readers who wanted, or rather demanded, to know where copies "suitable for framing" could be had.

The qualifications needed for the painting of such pictures are easily listed. To begin with the artist needs a great amount of astronomical knowledge. In fact he needs more than just knowledge; he has to have a thorough understanding of the problems involved. It is not just a question of being told that Saturn's rings consist of millions upon countless millions of tiny "moons," from the size of sand grains on up. It is a matter too of understanding why that has to be so, how it was deduced theoretically, how it was proved by observation, how sunlight will scatter under these circumstances. Nor does it hurt to know who worked on the theory and who did the observational work, and when, and where. And again, the artist has to know the laws of optics in principle and in detail, since the very first thing that will confront him is a little problem like this: the whole picture will correspond to a visual angle of 30 degrees; the object is 31,000 miles in diameter and will be seen from a distance of 220,000 miles; it will therefore subtend an angle of so and so many degrees, which will be how much in my picture? All these things, of course, are taught and can be learned. But then there is the requirement of a very special kind of technique, and that you either have or you don't. Add to all this an artistic eye, a fantastic amount of care, and the ability to integrate all these things into a whole, and you have an outline of the requirements.

The result is not an "artist's conception" but a picture which you might obtain if it were possible to get a very good camera with perfectly colour-true film into the proper position and have it manned by a good photographer who could use just the right exposure with the proper artistic touch.

It is obvious that this involves, not just a special talent coupled with special studies, but really an entire life history.

10

"The astronomical background began," I'm now quoting from a letter written by Chesley Bonestell, "when I was 10 years old and read Laplace's nebular hypothesis. I made many trips to Mount Hamilton Observatory. When the 100-inch telescope on Mount Wilson was completed I wrote to Dr. Hale, on the very thin excuse that my uncle's brother-in-law John Hooker had given the money for the mirror. He replied by sending me a portfolio of beautiful photographs of the moon. Through the years I have kept my interest in astronomy and made sketches and paintings to amuse the children of my friends. . . ."

Of course this is not the whole story. One first has to learn how to make sketches—if they are to be real sketches and not just approximate doodles on paper. That came about in a somewhat zigzaggy way:

"At 18 I studied at night at the Hopkins Art Institute of San Francisco and worked in the daytime in my grandfather's wholesale paper business. Realizing I was a complete flop as a businessman my grandfather compromised on the life of a painter by offering to send me to any college of my choosing to study architecture. I picked Columbia because it was the farthest from home and was fortunate in having Frank Dempster Sherman—poet and mathematician—to teach me perspective, shades and shadows and sterotomy. When I finished with him I could draw the reflections of a chair at a specific angle against a mirror tipped from the wall at a different angle. . . ."

The terms picked by Chesley Bonestell to characterize Frank D. Sherman might equally be applied now to his own painting, the product of a poetical mathematician with a paint brush. But at first the knowledge gained at Columbia was put to strictly practical use.

"It was natural that my painting ability should tie in with the perspective and I should enjoy a moderate reputation as a renderer with the leading architects of the time."

A "renderer," it should be explained for those who know little about architecture, is a man who takes design sketches and prints and produces from them a picture of the edifice-to-be which is then shown to the customer to convince him that the architect will really build something for his money.

"After the first World War I went to London where I worked as a special artist on the *Illustrated London News* and London evening papers. Returning to New York in 1927 I worked on most of the big skyscrapers, designing and rendering, until the depression brought construction to a halt in 1932. Then I went back to San Francisco which I always consider as home and worked on the war memorial buildings as director of colour. I also made the promotion drawings for the 1938 San Francisco Exposition. In addition I made a series of drawings and paintings, throwing sections of the Golden Gate bridge into perspective from the blueprints so that the directors could see how the bridge was to be built.

"I then turned my steps to Hollywood where I went to work for RKO as a sketch artist. At the end of the month we were all fired as work ran out but the head of the Art Department thought my photographic technique would be valuable in the trick department or, as they call it, 'Special Camera Effects.' All my life I had been fighting the 'tight' technique and trying to paint broadly. Now I found that the photographic technique was hard to find and valuable, so I went all out for it ever since."

Working on "special camera effects" the problem of "how large would this look if seen from such and such a distance with an over-all camera angle of so and so many degrees" came up in all seriousness. It has come up with many artists, but for Chesley Bonestell it quickly took on the shape of "if Titan is so and so many miles from Saturn, and Saturn so many miles in diameter, with the plane of the rings inclined so and so many degrees . . . what will be the result?" The result is Plate XXXVI.

And Plate XXXVI was the beginning of the book.

WILLY LEY

New York, May 1, 1949.

THE CONQUEST OF SPACE

THE PLANETS OF THE SOLAR SYSTEM

Planet	Mean distance from sun (million miles)	Length of year	Mean daily motion (degrees)	Eccentricity	Inclination to ecliptic
Mercury	36.0	88.0 days	4.092	0.2056	7° 0′ 12″
Venus	67.2	224.7 days	1.602	0.0068	3° 23′ 38″
Earth	93.0	365.25 days	0.986	0.0167	0° 0′ 0″
Mars	141.5	1.88 years	0.524	0.0933	1° 51′ 0″
Jupiter	483.3	11.86 years	0.083	0.0484	2° 29′ 29″
Saturn	886.1	29.46 years	0.034	0.0558	1° 18′ 26″
Uranus	1,782.8	84.02 years	0.012	0.0471	0° 46′ 22″
Neptune	2,793.5	164.79 years	0.006	0.0085	1° 46′ 37″
Pluto	3,675.0	248.43 years	0.004	0.2486	17° 08′ 38″

Planet	Orbital velocity (miles per second)	Escape velocity (miles per second)	Gravity at surface (earth=1)	Period of rotation	Inclination of equator to orbit
Mercury	29.7	2.2	0.27	88 days	near zero
Venus	21.7	6.3	0.85	unknown	unknown
Earth	18.5	7.0	1.00	1 day	23° 27′
Mars	15.0	3.1	0.38	24 hr. 37 min.	25° 10′
Jupiter	8.1	37.0	2.64	9 hr. 55 min.	3° 7′
Saturn	6.0	22.0	1.17	10 hr. 14 min.	26° 47′
Uranus	4.2	13.0	0.92	10 hr. 40 min.	98°
Neptune	3.4	14.0	1.12	15 hr. 40 min.	151°
Pluto	2.7 ?	6.5 ?	0.9 ?	unknown	unknown

Planet	Mass (earth=1)	Volume (earth=1)	Density (water=1)	Diameter (miles)	Diameter of iron sphere of equal weight (miles)	Albedo (per cent)
Mercury	0.04	0.055	2.86	3,100	2,410	7
Venus	0.8	0.876	4.86	7,700	6,540	59
Earth	1.0	1.000	5.52	7,900	7,040	50 ?
Mars	0.11	0.151	3.96	4,200	3,370	15
Jupiter	317.0	1,312.0	1.34	86,700	48,000	44
Saturn	95.0	763.0	0.71	71,500	32,120	42
Uranus	14.7	59.0	1.27	32,000	17,250	45
Neptune	17.2	72.0	1.58	31,000	18,160	52
Pluto	0.7	0.9 ?	5.3?	7,700 ?	6,500	15 ?

THE SATELLITES OF THE SOLAR SYSTEM

Planet	Satellite	Discoverer	Year of discovery	Mean distance from primary (miles)	Period of revolution (days)	Diameter (miles)
EARTH	Moon	Pithecan-thropus	very pre-historic	239,000	27.32	2,160
MARS	Phobos	Asaph Hall	1877	5,800	0.42	10
	Deimos	Asaph Hall	1877	14,600	1.26	5
JUPITER	V	Barnard	1892	112,600	0.50	100
	I, Io	Galilei	1610	261,800	1.77	2,300
	II, Europa	Galilei	1610	416,600	3.55	2,000
	III, Ganymede	Galilei	1610	664,200	7.15	3,200
	IV, Callisto	Galilei	1610	1,169,000	16.69	3,200
	VI	Perrine	1904	7,114,000	250.33	100
	VII	Perrine	1905	7,292,000	260	40
	X	Nicholson	1938	7,350,000	260	15 ?
	XI	Nicholson	1938	14,040,000	690	15 ?
	VIII	Melotte	1908	14,600,000	740	40
	IX	Nicholson	1914	14,880,000	760	20
SATURN[1]	Mimas	Herschel	1789	115,000	0.94	370
	Enceladus	Herschel	1789	148,000	1.36	460
	Tethys	Cassini	1684	183,000	1.89	750
	Dione	Cassini	1684	234,000	2.74	900
	Rhea	Cassini	1672	327,000	4.52	1,150
	Titan	Huyghens	1655	759,000	15.94	3,550
	Hyperion	Bond	1848	920,000	21.28	300
	Japetus	Cassini	1671	2,210,000	79.33	1,000
	Phoebe	Pickering	1898	8,034,000	550	200
	Themis	Pickering	1905	(existence doubtful)		
URANUS	nameless	Kuiper	1948	80,800	1.41	150 ?
	Ariel	Lassell	1851	119,100	2.52	600
	Umbriel	Lassell	1851	165,900	4.14	400
	Titania	Herschel	1787	272,000	8.71	1,000
	Oberon	Herschel	1787	364,000	13.46	900
NEPTUNE	"Triton"[2]	Lassell	1846	220,000	5.88	3,000
	nameless	Kuiper	1949	5,000,000	730	200

[1] The sizes of the satellites of the planets beyond Jupiter should be considered approximations only.

[2] For reasons I have been unable to discover, the name of Neptune's moon is not considered "official."

15

1. "FOUR, THREE, TWO, ONE. . . ROCKET AWAY!"

THE SKY is an endless dome of very clear and very blue glass. The innumerable sand hillocks of the desert are real only directly underfoot. The one you stand on is about 5 feet high and difficult to climb, and so are the others for 30 or 40 feet around. But beyond that distance they seem to be shallower and the dusty green sagebrush that grows on these hillocks does not look quite so dusty and dead. Still farther away all the hillocks seem to melt into one immense flat plain. Underfoot you have whitish-yellow sand, brownish-yellow sand, and the dusty green of the plants; in the distance there is just a faint impression of yellowish-white, overlaid with a greenish tinge.

Over all this, small heat waves are flickering. The sun, almost overhead, is a disk of white-hot steel that burns down on skin and cloth and shoeleather, on sand and sagebrush. It also burns down on the vertical bluish darkness that forms the mountains to the left. They seem within a half-hour's walk; actually they are some 20 miles away. Far over to the right, far even in this clear atmosphere, another darkish mountain chain fringes the horizon. A couple of the peaks are blinding white in the hot sun. And a sharp eye, guided mostly by accident, can detect a faint crescent in that blue sky. Conforming to astronomical theory, the bulge of that crescent points toward the sun. If the crescent were less faint, and the direct impact of the sun's rays on your exposed skin less violent, you could make a mental geometric experiment: connect the two horns by an imaginary line, bisect that line, and draw another line vertical to the first through that point. The part of the second line that passes through the bulge of the crescent will pass through the centre of the sun.

But your attention is not focused on the moon's crescent and only involuntarily on the solar disk. The near mountains to the left and the far mountains to the right are just backdrop. Your attention is focused on a point straight ahead, where there is a patch of concrete on the desert sand. In the centre of that patch is a small steel structure, really only a steel ring some 6 feet in diameter, supported by steel uprights so that it is about 4 feet above the concrete. Technicians have seen to it that this steel ring is perfectly horizontal. And on that steel ring, but not attached to it, stands a long rocket.

You are in the spectator's area of the White Sands Proving Ground. Geographically your position is almost due north of El Paso, Texas, and due east of Las Cruces, New Mexico, and the Organ Mountains. The distant mountains in the northeast are the Sacramento Mountains. You are 4000 feet above sea-level, but the highest peaks of those mountains reach another 6000 feet into the sky.

The rocket standing on the concrete apron of the firing table half a mile away will reach more than 600,000 feet into the sky, falling back to the ground some 25 miles north from its launching point. It will carry a "warhead," loaded with scientific instruments of all kinds, with an over-all weight of 1 ton. The rocket itself weighs 3 tons. Its two main fuel tanks hold over 8000 pounds of alcohol (containing 25 per cent water) and 11,000 pounds of liquid oxygen. Below these two main tanks, which constitute the bulk of the rocket, are two much smaller tanks, one holding 370 pounds of highly concentrated hydrogen peroxide, the other 30 pounds of potassium permanganate. When these two are brought together, steam, ordinary steam, is the result. The steam will drive a turbine and the turbine will drive a set of centrifugal pumps, delivering the main fuels to the rocket motor at the rate of 265 pounds per second.

So far everything is quiet. The rocket is fully fuelled. For miles around operators aim radar sets and special cameras, mounted in the manner of anti-aircraft guns, on the rocket. A short distance from the rocket, which stands still and vertical on its firing table—and by virtue of its weight would stand still and vertical even in a high wind—there is a blockhouse. A few years ago an army engineer was ordered to design an indestructible blockhouse. This is what that engineer designed—the concrete walls are 10 feet thick, and the pyramidal roof of reinforced concrete is 27 feet thick. Inside the blockhouse, at this instant, somebody writes X—4 on a blackboard. Four minutes to go.

Sixteen minutes ago a cloud of red smoke suddenly appeared over the blockhouse. It was the signal for everybody that the time was X—20: "Stand by for firing." There was a kind of frantic last-minute check-up then. Everything had been checked fifteen times before, but when that red smoke appeared the radar operators just could not help feeling the connections of their electric leads once more. The officer-in-charge checked once more to see whether the rocket was really vertical. Everybody looked once more at whatever he was in charge of. But then . . . waiting.

Suddenly there is a red star shell over the blockhouse. Everybody present knows that somebody just wrote X—2 on the blackboard inside. Now everybody is really tense. There are over 10,000 pints of liquid oxygen boiling in one tank in the rocket that stands under the hot sun of the desert. The magnetic clamp that holds some of the switches closed is still in place. Inside the big rocket motor there is an old-fashioned pyrotechnic pinwheel, the kind first invented 4 centuries ago, which provides ignition for the rocket after having itself been ignited electrically. So many things can still go wrong. What if the wire to the pinwheel has a poor connection somewhere? What if there is a power failure? Those gyros in the rocket? Everybody thinks of something that can go wrong—after all, the rocket itself is several years old. It was captured in a German underground factory, and then shipped to America. Each part has been loaded and unloaded a dozen times, and has travelled a total of 6000 miles.

Somebody writes X—1 on the blackboard.

If there is anything wrong, there is nothing anybody can do now. Fifty seconds to go. Forty seconds to go. Thirty seconds. Only twenty seconds now. An officer nods. Somebody else moves a hand weighted as if covered with a steel glove, which comes to rest on the ignition button.

The pinwheel burns.

Now the valves jump open, various sets of them in succession. Liquid oxygen and alcohol fall down through pipelines from the tanks into the motor. They catch fire. The visitors half a mile away hear a noise. It is a sound which cannot be described, for even the sound of a rocket motor is something that did not exist in the past. It is something like the steady roar of a waterfall blended with the grumble of a distant thunderstorm. Inside the rocket the peroxide and the permanganate come together, form steam, and begin to spin the turbine wheel. After 4 seconds the pumps move at full speed.

Inside the blockhouse somebody counts off seconds. "Six"—"Five"— "Four"—now the turbine is running—"Three"—"Two"—now the turbine-driven pumps *force* the fuels—"One"—the noise of the rocket has become incredible, deafening; impossible sound wave piled on impossible sound wave —"*Zero!*"—"Rocket away!"

The fire stream of the rocket, deflected by a steel pyramid inside the firing table, splashes for scores and scores of feet over the concrete apron. The sound is so intolerable that the ears do not protest any more. And the rocket is in the air, standing in an incredible manner on the stream of fire it ejects. The rocket is now as high as its own 46-foot length, the tip of the fire stream still touching the ground. But the rocket rises, slowly at first like an elevator, but gaining speed, not quite 40 feet per second for every second elapsed.

Radars and telescopic cameras rear up. The rocket is a mile high and the spectators realize that there is still a deafening sound beating upon their ears. They shake their heads violently, as if one could get rid of the roaring thunder that way. Now the rocket has reached an altitude of 3 miles. It is still clearly visible, still clearly audible, except perhaps to ears that have lost their sensitivity because of the noise of the preceding quarter-minute.

Ten miles above the Proving Ground. One cannot see the rocket clearly any more; the eyes follow the flame rather than the missile which emits it. The rocket is going faster and faster. It now adds much more than 40 feet per second to its speed.

During that so-called "preliminary stage" when the fuel just fell into the motor from the tanks, the motor produced a thrust of roughly 6 tons. Naturally a thrust of 6 tons does not move a rocket weighing between 12 and 13 tons. When the pumps began to work, the thrust jumped from 6 tons to 27 tons. It is still 27 tons, but the rocket has lost weight in the meantime. Every second, 265 pounds of fuel are burned and ejected in a fiery cascade which escapes from the motor with a velocity of 7000 feet per second. The rocket grows steadily lighter, but the thrust remains the same. Not only does its velocity keep increasing steadily, even its acceleration increases, because the figure for acceleration is the result of dividing the thrust by the weight.

20

Fifteen miles up.

The weight of the rocket still diminishes at the same rate. But now there is virtually no air resistance any more to hamper the movement of the rocket. And as the air pressure falls off the exhaust blast can emerge from the motor faster. Now the thrust is determined by the mass of the exhaust multiplied by the exhaust velocity. The mass of the exhaust remains the same, but the increased exhaust velocity increases the thrust. In empty space the thrust would be (and is) 15 per cent greater than the thrust at sea level. But acceleration is determined by dividing the thrust by the weight of the rocket. The rocket is now rather light. The acceleration is consequently high and the velocity has mounted incredibly. After 68 seconds of burning, the fuel supply is virtually exhausted, but the velocity of the rocket is 1 mile per second.

There is a mechanism in the rocket which shuts off the fuel flow when the desired velocity has been reached. Or one may simply exhaust the fuel supply. In either case, the instant when the flame of the rocket motor disappears is called "*Brennschluss,*" a German word which has become military English and will soon be ordinary English. The word had to be adopted, because its translation, "burnout," could mean *Brennschluss,* or it could mean that the motor itself had burned out—which would do crazy violence to the path of the rocket.

Naturally the rocket does not fall back at *Brennschluss.* A velocity of 1 mile per second is a considerable fortune in kinetic energy. The gravitational attraction of the earth reduces that fortune by not quite 32 feet per second of velocity during every second. Until the velocity has been eaten up at this rate the rocket continues to rise. It rises for another 100 seconds and to an altitude of around 110 miles before gravity wins and the rocket begins to fall back. Five minutes after take-off, within a few seconds' deviation, the rocket strikes the desert. It has travelled only about 30 miles horizontally, but along a trajectory that carried it 110 miles into the upper atmosphere.

A highly interesting trajectory—a most promising trajectory.

And now our scene shifts from the sun-warmed expanse of the Proving Ground to the enclosed space of the classroom. It is a class of advanced students and the professor has just drawn such a 110-mile-high and 30-mile-range trajectory on the blackboard. Professors, as a rule, do not draw like

Chesley Bonestell, but while the chalk curve lacks perfect beauty of symmetry it is clear enough. Moreover, the students know what it means. But then the professor asks the crucial question: "Mathematically speaking, this curve is what?"

And the class answers in unified conviction: "A parabola."

Which convinces the professor emotionally—so far he has known it only intellectually—that he is dealing with a new class and that he has to start all over again erasing simplifications which were justified in their place but should have been labelled as what they were when they were made. He explains patiently that it has been customary for at least a century to refer to the trajectory of an artillery projectile as a parabola. Mathematically this was rather simple. Air-resistance factors were put in empirically anyway. And calculation and experiment were in close agreement—as close, at least, as could be expected. But the underlying assumption all the time was that the line from gun to target was a straight line. As long as a 1-mile range was "great" and a 4-mile range "unbelievable," this was all right. But when you fire guns over 20 miles and rockets over 200 miles you have to admit the rather elementary fact that the earth is round. The line connecting battery and target is not straight but a curve, a part of a circle. And the curve along which the shell or rocket moves is not a parabola.

It is an ellipse.

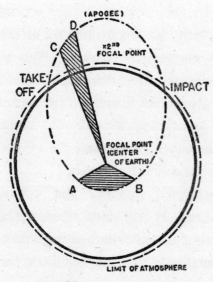

FIG. 1a. A Keplerian ellipse—incidentally the trajectory of a long-range missile or a space rocket. An ellipse has two focal points and in this case one of them coincides with the centre of the earth. According to Kepler's Second Law, the *radius vector*, which is the line from that focal point to any point of the ellipse, moves over equal areas during equal intervals of time. Therefore it would require as much time to cover the distance from C to D as it would require to cover the much longer distance from A to B, provided the latter were possible. It follows that the rocket is slowest at its apogee, the maximum distance from the surface. The second focal point, in this case located above the atmosphere, is of little practical importance. The closer the two points are together, the less eccentric the ellipse; if the two focal points coincide we get a circle.

As soon as one begins to deal with long-range trajectories it is not only practicable but virtually inevitable to leave all earthbound concepts behind and to approach the problems from the point of view of the astronomer. Out there in space the curve called a parabola is a mere abstraction. A comet might conceivably approach the sun along a parabolic orbit but it would be hard to find an astronomer willing to stake his reputation on a declaration that comet so-and-so actually did describe a mathematical parabola. Its orbit might have been a hyperbola. Much more likely it was a very long ellipse.

When it comes to movements in space, the ellipse is the ruling geometrical figure. The planets revolve around the sun in elliptical paths. The moons revolve around the planets in elliptical paths. A bean-sized meteorite which revolves around the sun describes this path as faithfully as does mighty Jupiter. The paths of periodic comets, like Halley's comet, are ellipses, just as are the orbits of the planets. The only difference is that the ellipses of the periodic comets are highly elongated while those of the major planets are almost circular. But they are always ellipses and they all obey the law discovered by Johannes Kepler some three centuries ago: the primary (general term for a

Fig. 1b. A parabola. As distinct from a circle or an ellipse, a parabola is not a closed figure. A circle is a curve where every point is equidistant from the centre. In an ellipse every point of the periphery has the same distance from both focal points, which means that the sum of the distances from both focal points is always the same figure for a given ellipse. A parabola has only one focal point (F) and every point P of the parabola is equidistant from F and from the line behind F. The parabola is the ideal shape for automobile headlamps, etc. It can easily be seen that the difference between a parabola and one end of a long ellipse might be hard to tell. Circle, ellipse, and parabola are three of the four so-called "conic sections." The fourth, the hyperbola, is also an open curve somewhat resembling the parabola. Heavenly bodies can theoretically move in any of the four, but circle and parabola are very rare exceptions, while ellipse and hyperbola are the rule: the former for planets, their satellites, and many comets; the latter for nonperiodic comets.

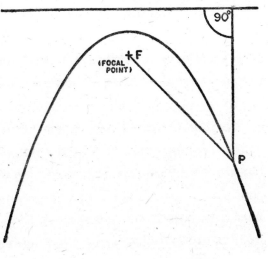

23

body around which another revolves) is always in one of the focal points of the ellipse. Kepler did not express it that way, because he was speaking of the orbits of planets only. He said that the sun is in the focal point, or rather in one of them, since an ellipse has two focal points. But it holds true for the moons too—in their cases the planet is in one of the focal points of their orbits. And when we send a V-2 rocket or any other large rocket on its journey into and beyond the stratosphere it follows Kepler's law as if it were a temporary moon.

Its trajectory is an ellipse and the centre of the earth is in one of the focal points of that ellipse. The ellipse is highly elongated and only a small part of it is actually traversed because the bulk of the planet interferes with the completion of the orbit. But it is an ellipse just the same. Nor does the relation between altitude above the ground and range measured along the ground alter this fact in any way.

At the White Sands Proving Ground in New Mexico, where the rockets carry instruments for scientific research, the preference is in favour of high altitude; consequently the range is comparatively short. In Europe, near the end of World War II, when the same kind of rocket was used for military purposes, it reached a maximum height above the ground of not quite 70 miles and a range of close to 200 miles. But in both cases the trajectory was the upper section of an ellipse with the centre of the earth in one of its focal points. The "White Sands ellipse" is exceptionally narrow and elongated; the "European war ellipse," seen as a whole, was shorter and fatter, but the orbit of a rocket always was, is, will be, and has to be an ellipse.

For a number of engineering reasons rockets were and are and probably always will be fired vertically. One of the engineering reasons is that a rocket designed to be fired vertically can be of lighter construction. Another and very important practical reason is that the rocket with a vertical firing quickly reaches highly attenuated layers of the atmosphere where air resistance becomes unimportant and finally nonexistent. But as soon as the rocket has traversed the densest atmospheric layers, a special mechanism tilts it slowly from the vertical. The "real" trajectory, in the mathematical sense, begins when a 45-degree tilt is completed. One may imagine the take-off manœuvre as a kind of preliminary curve for "easing" into the trajectory, somewhat like

24

manœuvring out of the driveway in order to get onto the highway. In war-time operational use it required the first 50 seconds of the V-2's 68 seconds' burning time to get the rocket into the proper path. At White Sands, where the tilt is much less, a much shorter time is needed.

Since the tilting should and does take place after the rocket has left the densest layers of the atmosphere, external fins or rudders cannot be used for this purpose. In the V-2 rocket the tilting is accomplished by having graphite vanes in the exhaust blast itself. As long ago as 1935 Professor Robert H. Goddard used vanes that touched the exhaust blast with their flat sides. He actually employed this mechanism for stabilizing his rockets on a vertical path, but it could also accomplish tilting. If the rocket were very large, and prefer-ably manned, one could think of separate smaller rocket motors to be used for positioning the rocket. Possibly a combination of such positioning jets and internal vanes will prove eventually to be the most practical method. In any event the problem can be solved.

Now that we have the question of the general shape of the trajectory straightened out, we can focus our attention on a few other elementary con-siderations. Suppose the problem is to obtain the longest possible horizontal range. The answer to that problem can be stated tersely in the language of the classroom by saying: The horizontal range is determined by the angle of the tilt and by the velocity at *Brennschluss*.

This statement, worded differently, has been with us for a longer number of years than any individual can remember. It can be found in any old training manual or instruction manual for artillery officers, where it reads: The range depends on the elevation of the gun and on the muzzle velocity of the ball. That a gun pointing upward produced a longer range than one placed hori-zontally must have been one of the early gunner's discoveries. And in about 1540 an Italian by the name of Tartaglia began to make systematic experi-ments, which led to the conclusion that a gun elevation of 45 degrees produced maximum range. If the elevation was less, the ball struck the ground too soon. (We would say that the ellipse of the trajectory was intersected too quickly by the circle formed by the earth's surface.) If the elevation was more, the ball rose to unnecessary heights. (Today we would express that by saying that the two intersection points on the ellipse are too close to each other when

25

measured along the circle of the earth's surface, because of the high eccentricity of the ellipse involved.) Tartaglia also found that in a 45-degree shot the peak altitude reached by the ball was one-fourth of its range. He did not know that the maximum range was twice what the altitude would have been if the gun had been fired vertically.

For maximum range, then, we need a tilt of 45 degrees. (In actual practice there are often deviations from this angle for various reasons.) And if we want a long range we must also see to it that the velocity at *Brennschluss* is as high as possible. To accomplish the latter there are essentially two methods. One is to have a fuel with a very high exhaust velocity, since the velocity attained by the rocket varies with the exhaust velocity of the fuel for a given fuel load. This method, obviously, finds its limit in the nature (more precisely: the energy content) of the fuels at the disposal of the designer. The other method is to have a very high fuel load. Suppose we divide the take-off weight of a rocket loaded with fuel by its remaining weight (the rocket itself plus its payload) after the fuel has been used up. We then get a figure which is technically known as the mass-ratio. In the case of the V-2 rocket that mass-ratio happens to be very nearly 3:1.[1]

Of the whole mathematical demonstration in the footnote the layman can be satisfied with the last sentence, namely, that the velocity at *Brennschluss* will be the same as the exhaust velocity if the mass-ratio is 2.7:1—that is, if the rocket at take-off weighs 2.7 times as much as its empty hull, machinery, and payload. The fact that V-2 with a mass-ratio of 3:1 does not reach its own exhaust velocity at *Brennschluss* (its velocity is slightly above 1600 metres per second, while its exhaust velocity is 2100 metres per second) is accounted for

[1] In the classroom the professor has meanwhile obligingly put the basic equations on the blackboard. Calling the mass of the rocket itself M_R, the mass of the payload M_P and the mass of the fuel load M_F, he calls the sum $M_R + M_P + M_F = M_0$ which is the take-off mass. Logically, then, $M_R + M_P = M_1$, or the "remaining mass," so that M_0/M_1 expresses the mass-ratio.

Now the thrust of the rocket motor (which he calls P) equals the product of exhaust velocity (called c) multiplied by a so-called "differential" dm/dt, which we will take to mean the fuel consumption per second. Hence the formula for the thrust of the motor comes out as $P = c \cdot dm/dt$ and from this formula he can derive, in a manner mathematicians find simple, that the maximum velocity v of the rocket must follow the equation $v = c \cdot lognat\ M_0/M_1$ from which he derives (even more simply, virtually elementary, friends!) that $M_0/M_1 = e^{v/c}$. Or, by way of example, if the required velocity is 2 miles per second and the exhaust velocity happens to be 2 miles per second, the mass-ratio will be

$$M_0/M_1 = e^{2/2} = e = 2.72.$$

This means that a rocket will attain a velocity equal to its own exhaust velocity if its mass-ratio is 2.72:1, provided that all this takes place in "ideal space."

by air resistance and the fight against gravity. That mathematical relationship on the blackboard is true only for "ideal space," which means a thoroughly unrealistic space in which there is neither air nor a gravitational field.

But it is a fact that the difference between the performance in "ideal space" and in real space becomes smaller and smaller the larger the rocket and the longer the range. In a rocket capable of reaching the moon that difference might be as little as 5 per cent.

This whole explanation is intended to show that it would be easier to increase the range of a rocket if we could fill it up with a fuel that produces a higher exhaust velocity. But once the limit of exhaust velocity of available fuels has been reached, it is still possible to increase the range by increasing the mass-ratio of the rocket—in other words, its fuel load. To give just one example, let us assume that the problem is to fire a rocket over a range of 600 miles, three times the range of V-2. The velocity of the rocket would have to be about 10,500 feet per second. Say that the exhaust velocity of the fuel in that rocket amounts to "only" 6600 feet per second. It can still be done if the mass-ratio of the rocket equals about 4.5:1. But this is for "ideal space," which certainly does not prevail near the earth. Allowing for actual conditions, we have to add about 30 per cent to the figure just given, so that the mass-ratio really needed would be 6:1. A rocket with such a mass-ratio has not yet been built, but nobody doubts that it can be done with some more practice.

If, however, we could push the exhaust velocity to something like 10,000 feet per second (which is also possible, although not easily accomplished at present) the mass-ratio, with some allowances for actual conditions, would have to be only about 3.6:1, not much higher than the 3:1 mass-ratio of V-2.

The foregoing statements and explanations cover the main principle, which is simply that high performance depends on high velocity, and that velocity, in turn, is determined by mass-ratio and by exhaust velocity. The bulk of rocket engineering has to do with the practical problems of producing a high mass-ratio and of creating a high exhaust velocity.

But in this particular case, the case of a long-range shot from one point on the surface of our planet to another point on its surface, there exists an additional possibility. Or, rather, there is room for an additional trick. The rocket's range can be considerably extended by the use of wings.

27

This is a statement that cannot, or at least should not, be made without an explanation following hard upon its heels. The mental picture created by the term "winged long-range rocket" is inevitably drawn from the brain's store of aeroplane pictures. The term seems to be just a fancy one for an aeroplane in which a rocket motor has been substituted for a more conventional power plant. The mental picture is likely to resemble an enlarged version of the experimental rocket aeroplane XS-1. What makes the situation worse is that the winged long-range rocket of the future actually will resemble the XS-1 aeroplane.

In spite of this resemblance there is an enormous difference in concept and in principle between a rocket aeroplane and a winged rocket. The difference does not show so much in external shape, or even in internal engineering design. It is essentially in the manner of handling the vehicle.

One can best approach the difference in concept by considering the way an ordinary aeroplane gains altitude. In aeroplanes propelled by internal-combustion engines, or turbojets, or turboprops, the direction of propulsion is essentially horizontal. This creates an air flow around the wing and this air flow produces lift. Naturally, since the aeroplane is a body moving through the air, the wings also create air resistance, or drag. That cannot be helped; the drag is the price you have to pay for the lift. Because the wings actually carry the plane, the thrust produced by propellers or turbojets can be and is less than the weight of the plane.

But if we tried to imitate this performance with a rocket motor as a power plant we would quickly find ourselves in a strange dilemma. The efficiency of the rocket motor depends on the velocity with which it is permitted to move. If the rocket motor runs with little thrust in order to imitate the operation, say, of a fast jet plane, the result would be a run at very low efficiency, an enormous waste of fuel, and the probability of very quickly reaching a point where there is no space left for additional fuel. The alternate choice would be to run the rocket motor with a high thrust in order to attain a high velocity quickly so that the over-all efficiency is improved. But then the drag produced by the wings will be such that the aid they give by producing lift becomes unimportant.

With all this we still have to remember two points: that the thrust of the rocket motor can be, and in all probability will be, greater than the take-off weight of the vehicle, and that the job the wings *could* do is merely to carry the vehicle to an altitude where air density is so low that the wings no longer produce lift at all. If we remember in addition to this that a wingless rocket would attain the same altitude with generally better efficiency and hence with less fuel consumption we begin to realize that it is the scheme of operation which is wrong.

The thing to do is to propel such a vehicle almost vertically at take-off, to let the rocket motor do the lifting of the whole. In a vertical or near-vertical take-off the denser layers of the atmosphere are traversed in the shortest possible time. The wings would probably act as stabilizers in such a take-off, but they are "saved" for later use.[1]

The principle of the winged rocket may be stated by saying that such a vehicle is a rocket during take-off and during most of the trip along a rocket trajectory, and that it becomes an aeroplane, specifically a high-speed glider, upon re-entering the denser layers of the atmosphere. The performance, then, would be comparable to a V-2 performance in the early stages of a trip. The winged rocket would take off vertically (or nearly so) and at an altitude of about 8 miles or higher the rocket would be tilted just like a wingless rocket and roar into a normal elliptical trajectory. Even though the winged rocket will be in a more or less horizontal position up there it will not really "fly," since for any trip over a reasonably long distance the rocket will be outside the atmosphere. Technically the atmosphere of the earth extends to a distance of about 250 miles, but at about 150,000 to 200,000 feet the density is so low that the "air" is a better vacuum than that of an ordinary vacuum tube.

It is on the descending leg of the trajectory that the wings begin to assume a rôle. Until about a 150,000-foot altitude is reached again they might as well not be there. But from then on they begin to perform. A wingless rocket coming down on such a trajectory, would fall faster and faster and turn steeper and steeper, hitting the ground at a 90-degree angle. The winged rocket will leave the trajectory and assume a rather flat and immensely long glide path.

[1] The ideal would be, of course, to have folding wings which can be retracted into the body for take-off. But it seems that folding wings of great strength present such a knotty design problem that almost any other solution would be more easy of accomplishment.

Instead of increasing its speed in falling, it will decrease speed, since the speed is converted into lift.

This is how the performance of a winged rocket will differ (and must differ) from the performance of aeroplanes, whether the latter are propelled by internal-combustion engines, turbines, turbojets, or even athodyds. The aeroplane has to have power all the way. The rocket vehicle uses power to attain altitude and speed; kinetic energy and the laws of Nature do the rest.

Before we progress to the next chapter and leave the earth behind us completely, one more possibility has to be mentioned. So far we have considered only rockets which begin to expend their fuel at take-off and go on expending it until there is virtually none left. This performance will always lead to a Keplerian ellipse with the earth's centre in one focal point. What would happen if some fuel were saved until the rocket had about reached the peak of its trajectory, outside the atmosphere?

To answer this question we have to assume the astronomer's viewpoint again and acquaint ourselves with two astronomical terms. The earth, as we know, travels around the sun in an ellipse, the sun being at one of the focal points. We also know that the distance of earth to sun is not always the same; at one point of the earth's orbit we are closest to the sun, at another point farthest from the sun. Deriving his terms from the Greek word for the sun god, *Helios*, the astronomer calls the point of closest approach "perihelion" and the point of farthest distance "aphelion." When the earth instead of the sun becomes the reference point the Greek word for the earth, *gaia*, is utilized in the same way, and astronomers say of the moon that it is in "perigee" or in "apogee." In a rocket orbit, the peak of the trajectory is obviously the apogee while the perigee is buried somewhere beneath the earth's surface and is not actually reached.

If the pilot of a rocket uses power again when in or near apogee he changes his orbit (*see* Fig. 2). His elongated ellipse is changed into a far less eccentric ellipse that might look almost like a circle. His apogee will probably stay roughly where it was, but his perigee will move. Prior to the restoration of power, the perigee was quite close to the earth's centre; now it moves away from it. If it moves far enough it will actually emerge from the solid ball of

30

the earth into the atmosphere. And if it moves out of the atmosphere, it can even happen that the perigee changes places with the former apogee—that what was originally the most distant point of the ellipse becomes the lowest point on the new ellipse. The elliptical trajectory now deserves to be given the astronomical designation of "orbit." Since every part of that orbit is outside the earth's atmosphere the whole of it can be travelled by the rocket. Once such an orbit has been established no additional fuel need be expended; the rocket will, in fact, have become an artificial moon.

I hasten to add that this is a simplified explanation, designed only to show how such an orbit around the earth could be produced at all. When this experiment is actually made, it would be more efficient by far not to introduce the interval of powerless coasting which reduces the rocket's velocity, but to go into such an orbit "in one continuous sweep." The manœuvre would require a rocket velocity of just about 5 miles per second, which is about three times the highest velocity produced up to the moment of writing. But nobody doubts any more that it can be done.

Such an "orbital rocket" would be a rather useful instrument in many respects. By its mere presence it could serve as a reference point for navigational purposes—be it the navigation of a ship, an aeroplane, or a missile—and the stability of its orbit over a period of time, say a few years, would give a valuable indication of the density of matter in space. The matter referred to is not simply meteoric matter; there is some reason to suspect that there might be occasional clouds of ionized hydrogen in space. If this is the case it should influence the orbital rocket. But the orbital rocket would probably be equipped with telemetered instruments, which would provide designers on the ground with information on a lot of things that they want to know about.

In all probability the unmanned orbital rocket will be succeeded by a manned "station in space." The construction of this station would begin with a large manned rocket which would be put into such an orbit. Additional material could then be brought up to enlarge the ship which is there, and the station would grow out of the first rocket. Because of the special conditions prevailing on such a station (infinite vacuum, permanent apparent weightlessness, the possibility of creating any extreme of temperature either by concentrating the sun's rays or shielding something from the sun's rays), it could well be a most valuable laboratory. And it would also be a watchdog for the whole planet. Finally, it could be a refuelling place for rocket ships.

A ship which wanted to return from the station to earth would not be able to do so without some expenditure of fuel. But this expenditure would be far less than that required to go from the earth's surface to the station. The pilot would take off from the station in the direction opposite to its movement. That would produce an orbit for him which has its perigee inside the atmosphere. Air resistance will do the rest, and in the end he would land as if returning from the apogee of a transcontinental trip.

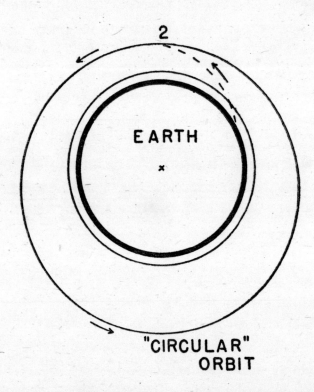

FIG. 2. Changeover to "circular" orbit. If power is again applied at or near the apogee of the ascending ellipse (dotted line) the rocket will go into an orbit around the earth, actually elliptical in shape but usually called a "circular" orbit. The perigee of this orbit is at point 2. The thin line close to earth marks the limit of earth's atmosphere.

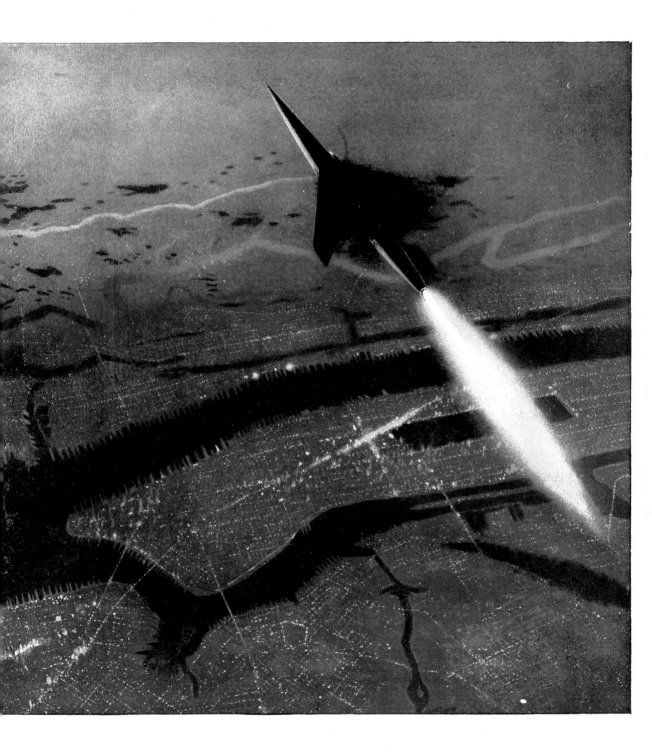

I. Transcontinental rocket ship taking off from Long Island airport for the West Coast, is now 10 miles above Manhattan, where it is dark, but the ship is going to overtake the sun. It took off almost vertically; is tilting itself into 45-degree angle for maximum range. At this instant the angle of its longitudinal axis is 49 degrees.

II. Twenty-five miles above New Jersey. All of Long Island is visible.

V. Flying to Europe from Long Island, a similar ship is 200 miles above the Atlantic, near the limits of the earth's atmosphere. Long Island and the New Jersey coast are clearly visible. The white spots that look like snow on the ground are actually cloud formations.

VI. Circling the earth outside the atmosphere, the passengers have a look at England at sunset. In the far distance, near the top of the picture, the Italian boot can be seen extending into the Mediterranean Sea. At the time when the Mediterranean was the centre of the civilized world, man had just progressed to the point of recognizing the moon as a solid "earthy" world like his own planet, which he already knew to be spherical.

38

VII. Two thousand miles above the surface of the earth, a sight which people will see during the first trip around the moon and which may be photographed before that from unmanned test missiles. Most of the visible area is Atlantic Ocean, with the Gulf of Mexico showing at the left. The black dot in space near the sun is the moon.

Chesley Bonestell ©

VIII. Four thousand miles above the surface of the earth, looking west. Africa is at the left, the Mediterranean Sea to the right of the North African coast. The outline of Europe is clearly visible, but appears somewhat distorted because we are used to seeing it on a flat map.

40

2. TARGET FOR TONIGHT: LUNA!

A BODY is falling through space.

It is a small mass of iron with a high percentage of nickel plus traces of other elements. Nobody knows where it came from originally, but it moved around the sun with the planets, its velocity determined solely by its distance from the sun, not by its own mass. On one side it was warmed by the rays of the sun, on the other side it radiated the heat received toward the distant stars of the outer rim of the galaxy. It happened that the body slowly rotated, so it was not always the same side that was heated by the sun's rays. Consequently the body attained a general equilibrium temperature all the way through. Since it was about the same distance from the sun as the planet earth is, its equilibrium temperature was what human beings would have called endurable—slightly above the melting point of ice, around 45 degrees Fahrenheit. Were it not for a few shiny and metallic and therefore reflecting surfaces it would have been some 15 degrees warmer.

One day the body was caught in the gravitational field of the earth. The earth was not a long distance away, as distances go in astronomical matters, roughly half a million miles. The gravitational field of the earth is quite weak at that distance but it does exert a little influence, for the gravitational field of a planet never really stops, it merely grows weaker and weaker with distance. If it has a certain strength, or value, at a given distance, it has only one-fourth of that value at double the distance, one-ninth of that value at thrice the distance, one-sixteenth at four times the distance, and so on. The gravitational field, as can be seen, weakens rather rapidly, but it finds its "end" or "limit" not by distance alone but because at some point the field of another body grows stronger.

The first day the field of the earth began to act on the small mass of nickel-iron it moved that mass scarcely as much as an inch. During the second day it moved it a little more and after some time the speed had increased to as much as a mile a day. And the deeper the body fell into the earth's field the stronger that field grew. When it was still several earth diameters from the surface of our planet, it had reached a velocity of 1 mile per second.

Now it is falling fast, with steadily increasing velocity. Two miles per second, soon afterwards 3 miles per second, then 4 and 5 miles per second. When it enters the top layers of the atmosphere, some 250 miles above the earth's surface, it moves with a velocity of 7 miles per second. The remaining distance to the ground is too short to increase that speed very much, even if no air were in the way. But there is air, and the meteorite compresses the air in its path like the piston of a Diesel engine (the air cannot get out of its way because the speed of the meteorite is many times the maximum speed at which air can move) and heats it by compression. The heat of the air is in part transferred to the meteorite and it begins to glow. The people on the ground call it a shooting star.

Any other planet could have been used in the example, but only for earth does the figure of 7 miles per second hold true. If the meteorite had made its long fall toward the planet Mars it would have arrived with a velocity of a little above 3 miles per second. If Jupiter had been the target, the velocity of arrival would have been 37 miles per second, and if it had been our moon, the velocity of arrival would have been slightly less than $1\frac{1}{2}$ miles per second.

Each planet, therefore, produces a velocity of arrival for a fall from very long distances which is typical and which is in fact an expression of the potency of its gravitational field. What is of practical importance is that this "velocity of arrival" also represents the "velocity of liberation." To revert to the language of chapter 1: the apogee of the trajectory of a rocket departing from earth with a velocity of 7 miles per second lies at an "infinite" distance from the perigee. In this sentence the word "infinite" should be understood in about the same sense as is signified by this word on the focal adjustment of a camera. It includes the mathematical meaning of the word, but it does not refer to mathematical infinity only. It means any really long distance. As far as the gravitational field of the earth alone is concerned, the trajectory of a rocket which attains a velocity of 7 miles per second at *Brennschluss* (outside the atmosphere, of course) will carry to any distance desired.

It is only natural that we should think first of the moon when reading a statement of this kind. Next to the sun, the moon, in naked-eye astronomy, is the most conspicuous body in the sky. The moon has, by pure chance, the same *apparent* diameter as the sun, namely about $\frac{1}{2}$ degree of arc, the 180th part of a right angle. But it is not size alone that has made the moon conspicuous, and in some respects even more interesting than the sun. Unlike the sun, which only changes its position in the sky, the moon also shows phases, which incidentally provided the first means of measuring time beyond the duration of a single day, from sunset to sunset. What adds still more interest is that there are visible spots on the moon.

Small wonder, then, that all the speculations, thoughts, and dreams which we are now tempted to label the "prehistory of space travel," concerned the moon and the moon only. They range all the way from the satyrical imaginings of Lukian of Samosata (Lucian), who in about A.D. 160 told the story of the mobilization of a large army on the moon, commanded by Endymion himself, to the "Moon Hoax" of Locke in 1835, when the *New York Sun* informed its readers in many instalments about marvellous discoveries which allegedly had been made on the moon by Sir John Herschel.

Even though it is general knowledge now that the moon is by no means a hospitable world it has lost none of its old fascination. One may know that Jupiter is the largest of the planets of our solar system, one may have seen the unearthly beauty of Saturn's rings in a telescope, one may have read volumes on the mystery of Mars—the moon is still the first thought when space travel is mentioned, because the moon is "a world" to the naked eye.

The figures are easily written down: diameter of the moon 2160 miles (earth, 7913 miles), average density 3.33 (earth 5.52), gravity at surface one-sixth that of earth, maximum distance from earth (apogee) 253,000 miles, minimum distance (perigee) 222,000 miles, average centre-to-centre distance 239,000 miles, escape velocity 1.47 miles per second, orbital velocity 0.64 miles per second. To this we may add the figure for the "albedo." Albedo, originally a Spanish word meaning "whiteness," somehow got into astronomical language, in which it means the ratio of the total amount of sunlight reflected (in all directions) from a spherical body to the amount received by the body. Jupiter, for example, has an albedo of 44 per cent, Venus one of 59 per cent. The albedo of the moon is only 7 per cent, which is about that of slate and lava and similar darkish rocks. In spite of its apparent brilliance the moon must consist essentially of rather dark rocks.

The figures applying to a moon trip by rocket are almost as commonplace now as the astronomical data just quoted. Of course, they are general figures which have to be taken with a grain of salt, because precise figures could be established only for a specific moonship. If we assume that the average acceleration of a moonship amounts to 4 g (" gravities "), which is something we are sure the pilot can stand, it would require around 500 seconds of acceleration to get the ship to a velocity of 7 miles per second. Then the ship would coast upward against the pull of earth's gravitation which would slowly reduce its velocity. Zero velocity would be reached after 300,000 seconds, but the distance traversed during this interval of time would amount to nine-tenths of the surface-to-surface distance between earth and moon. And that is also the distance at which we find the famous "dividing line" or "neutral point" where the gravitational forces of earth and moon are equal. If the ship crosses this "dividing line," no matter how slowly it is travelling, it will be removed from the earth's gravitational grip and be in that of the moon instead. It will begin to fall toward the moon, reaching its surface after another 50,000 seconds and striking it with a velocity of almost precisely 2 miles per second, a velocity which is the sum of the moon's escape velocity and its orbital speed.

If the ship is manned, that 2-mile-per-second velocity has to be counteracted by means of the rocket motors, since there is no atmosphere that could be used for braking. The fuel expenditure for this manœuvre would be the same as for a take-off from the moon. The same amount of fuel is required to reduce an existing velocity to zero as to accelerate from zero to that velocity. Hence a moonship has to be capable of the velocity changes shown in the table on the next page.

	Miles per second
Take-off from earth	7
Landing on the moon	2
Take-off from the moon	2
Allowance for corrections, etc.	1
	——
	12

This still presupposes that the landing on return can be accomplished without any expenditure of fuel—one may assume that the necessary techniques were worked out with long-range winged rockets and space rockets before we got around to building the moonship.

Those formulas mentioned in the footnote on page 26 enable us to tell what the mass-ratio should be for such a performance. Here, unfortunately, we are due to experience a bad shock. If we have a fuel with an exhaust velocity of only 1 mile per second, the mass-rotio becomes 163,100:1, an almost incredible figure which can be dismissed without a second glance as impossible. If we have a fuel with an exhaust velocity of 2 miles per second the mass-ratio drops a large number of notches and becomes 402:1. Of course such a mass-ratio is still a technical impossibility, but of a lesser order, so to speak. And an exhaust velocity of 2 miles per second has been obtained experimentally on occasion. It is by no means the rule yet, but it has been done. If we now go on to hope that one day an exhaust velocity of 3 miles per second will be obtained, the mass-ratio for a moonship which can land on the moon, take off again, and return to earth, drops to 54.6:1. Imagining an exhaust velocity of 4 miles per second we find a mass-ratio of 20:1, which begins to sound as if it were within the realms of possibility.

At this point it is desirable to follow another branch of reasoning for a moment. Obviously we would not send a manned ship to the moon—even if we could build one now—without preliminary experiments. The first of these would be, of course, to send an unmanned rocket to the moon and let it crash, providing it with some means of marking the spot of arrival in an unmistakable manner so that it could be seen with a telescope.[1] For that experiment we

---

[1] The moon's low albedo is most helpful here. A quantity of powdered gypsum or powdered glass blown around by the impact would produce a fine permanent mark.

45

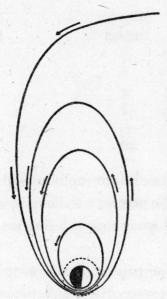

FIG. 3. "Braking ellipses" for landing on earth without fuel expenditure. The procedure, as it is contemplated at present, would be for the ship to "miss" the earth by a little more than 200 miles. The small amount of air resistance encountered in the top layers of the atmosphere would be enough to change the ship's orbit into a closed ellipse with its apogee at the point of "grazing." After completing a full ellipse about the earth the ship would enter the atmosphere again at the same point, lose some more velocity and perform a similar but shorter second ellipse. After several grazings the velocity would be reduced so much that the ship would not leave the atmosphere again but would land in a long spiral. Drawing is to scale, except that the atmosphere (broken circle) is about four times too deep. Length of directional arrows indicates velocity.

(From *Rockets and Space Travel*)

would need a velocity of only 7 miles per second, provided that this is attained outside the atmosphere. For a velocity of 7 miles per second, the mass-ratio would be 33:1 for an exhaust velocity of 2 miles per second, 10.2:1 for one of 3 miles per second, and 5.75:1 for a fuel with an exhaust velocity of 4 miles per second. Obviously such a rocket, which will crash on the moon (let's use the term Moon Messenger as a designation for this kind of performance), is more nearly within reach of present-day technology. One might even be optimistic enough to tackle the job with a fuel of 2-mile-per-second exhaust velocity.

The mass-ratio of 33:1 which would be required (or a mass-ratio in that general neighbourhood) is of course too large to be attained directly. The layman may dream of a rocket which has a take-off weight of 33 tons for every ton of remaining weight, but the designing engineer would not touch the job and would indeed gladly furnish the applicant with the addresses of his competitors.

But the rocket engineers' bag of tricks is not yet empty. The way out was impressively demonstrated on February 24, 1949, on the White Sands Proving Ground. On that day a V-2 carried, not its usual 1-ton warhead, but a smaller rocket of the type WAC Corporal. When the V-2 had reached its

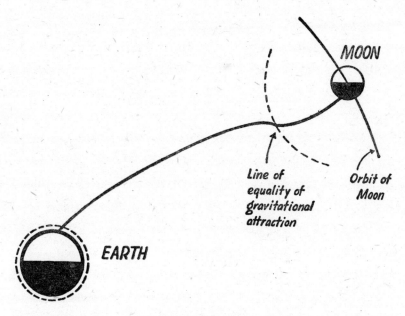

FIG. 4. Orbit of unmanned moon rocket. Earth and moon are drawn to scale, but should be eight times as far apart as shown. If the orbit of the rocket were drawn to scale, it would look like a straight line.

(From *Rockets and Space Travel*)

maximum velocity (and had exhausted its fuel supply), the smaller WAC Corporal took over, while the V-2 dropped back. The smaller rocket finished up at an altitude of 250 miles, to all intents and purposes outside the atmosphere. This method is technically known as the "step principle." Obviously the velocities of the individual steps are added together. But if you try to calculate the mass-ratio which would belong to the sum of the velocities you get a figure which is the product of the individual mass-ratios. It works as if the individual mass-ratios had been multiplied by one another. The result of that multiplication has been named "ideal mass-ratio," the term "ideal" to be understood in the sense of something that has no "real" existence. But the results are real enough.

Needless to say, the step principle changes the whole picture. What is impossible with a single rocket may be quite easy with a two-step rocket. A mass-ratio of 4:1 would not be too hard to achieve. However, a two-step rocket with two individual 4: 1 mass-ratios corresponds to a 16: 1 mass-ratio, which nobody would attempt to attain directly. And a two-step rocket with two individual 6: 1 mass-ratios would produce an "ideal" mass-ratio of 36: 1.

Naturally this is a simplified explanation. In reality the picture would be

47

somewhat more complicated, because one would use a few additional tricks. For example, it was mentioned in chapter 1 that the efficiency of a rocket motor depends on the velocity with which it is permitted to move. Therefore it may be more efficient, in the over-all picture, to use a fuel with a lesser exhaust velocity in the generally slower first step and a different fuel with a higher exhaust velocity in the generally faster second step. Take-off would be by booster unit, and there would be a few other complications. There would also be a lot of new problems of all kinds, leading to torn sketches and torn hair in the engineering department and also leading to the loudly expressed realization that a bricklayer has a nice simple life, especially when compared for example with an engineer who . .

In general, however, the Moon Messenger is close enough to present technological accomplishments so that its design and construction are possible without any *major* inventions. Its realization is essentially a question of hard work and money.

The manned moonship is a different story. The performance expected of it is, naturally, that it take off from earth, go to the moon, land, take off from the moon, and return to earth. And that, considering known chemical fuels and customary design and construction methods, is beyond our present ability. But while the moonship which can make a round trip is unattainable with chemical fuels, a moonship which can land on the moon with a fuel supply insufficient for the return is a remote possibility. The point here is that one more extension of the step principle is possible. Three ships which landed might have enough fuel left among them for one to make the return trip.

This, of course, involves great risk, since the failure of one ship would doom them all. Probably the manned moonship will have to be postponed until there is an orbital station. Take-off from the station, instead of from the ground, would require only an additional 2 miles per second, so that the total works out to about 7 miles per second, instead of the 12 miles per second mentioned on page 44.

Then, of course, there is the possibility of using atomic energy. If, some 15 years ago, a sceptical audience had been polled as to which of the two "impossibilities"—moonship and large-scale controlled release of atomic energy —they considered less fantastic, the poll would probably have been 100 per cent in favour of the moonship. As history turned out, atomic energy came first, and it is now permissible to speculate whether the one may not be the key to the other.

So far, unfortunately, we only know that elements like uranium, plutonium, etc., contain enough energy for the job. We also know that this energy is not completely inaccessible, that it can be released. It can even be released in two ways, either fast in the form of a superexplosion, or slowly in a so-called "pile" where the energy appears mainly as heat. But we don't know how to apply these phenomena to rocket propulsion. Obviously the fissionable matter should not form the exhaust; there should be an additional *reactant*, a substance which is thrown out: plain water, perhaps, which would appear as steam, possibly even split up into its component atoms of hydrogen and oxygen, or perhaps peroxide.

The "how" is still to be discovered, but it will probably be based on the principle of using a fissionable element's energy for the ejection of a relatively inert reactant. It may be that, when that problem has been solved, we will find a parallel to the problem of the pumps in an ordinary liquid-fuel rocket. When liquid-fuel rockets were still small—that was only about 17 years ago and I remember them vividly—the fuels were forced into the rocket motor by pressurizing the whole fuel tank. But everybody knew then that this would not do for all time to come. The tank that had to stand the feeding pressure had to have strong walls. Consequently it was heavy. Consequently the mass-ratio could not be small. The idea then was that the tank should be only strong enough to hold the fuels, in the manner of the gasoline tank of a car or a truck or an aeroplane, and that the feeding pressure should be furnished by a pump. Of course the pumps had to weigh less than the saving in tank-wall weight which they brought about. Obviously there was a minimum size and weight for a good pump, and if that minimum weight was rather large, a rocket with pumps would have to be a big rocket.

It happened just that way. Efficient pumps *were* large and heavy and the rocket with pumps was the 46-foot V-2. The "atomic motor" for rockets may also turn out to be large; the smallest really reliable and efficient model may be a compact little 7-ton unit. This would make for a large rocket—but the size of a vehicle is no obstacle if you have the power to move it.

49

Whatever the exhaust velocity, it will be high—an expectation of 5 miles per second may be conservative. With such an exhaust velocity the mass-ratio of the moonship would be 11 : 1; with an exhaust velocity of 10 miles per second the mass-ratio would drop to 3.3 : 1!

The moonship shown in the paintings of the second illustration section is based on the assumption of a mass-ratio of this order of magnitude, which in turn is based on the assumption of an atomic rocket motor.

Naturally there would be some trouble with radioactivity in an atomic-propelled rocket. But that is not quite as hard to handle as the radioactivity which would accompany atomic-energy proplusion under different circumstances. A seagoing vessel propelled by atomic energy could probably be built right now. It would operate by means of an atomic pile running at a temperature high enough to convert its cooling water into steam. The steam would drive a turbine, which would be coupled to the ship's propeller. While all this mechanism would be reasonably small and light as ship engines go, it would have to be encased in many tons of concrete to shield the ship's company against the radiation that would escape from the pile and from the water and steam that cool it. For a spaceship, no all-around shielding would be needed, only a single layer, separating the pilot's or crew's cabin in the nose from the rest of the ship. On the ground a ship which had grown "hot" through service would be placed inside a shielding structure, something like massive concrete walls, open at the top. That would provide complete shielding for the public, but a shielding that the ship would not have to carry.

The problem that may be more difficult to handle is that of the radio-activity of the exhaust. A moonship taking off would leave behind a radioactive patch, caused by the ground splash. Most likely that radioactivity would not last very long, but it would be a temporary danger spot. Obviously moonships for some time to come will begin their journeys from desolate places. Of course they might take off by means of booster units producing nothing more dangerous in their exhausts than water vapour, carbon dioxide, and maybe a sulphurous smell.

A good literary comparison stays with us, no matter how the accompanying ideas may change. That old writer Lukian of Samosata who produced the first story of a trip to the moon 1800 years ago thought that the earth's atmosphere also enveloped the moon. Consequently the trip occurred because a powerful storm out in the Atlantic, west of the Pillars of Hercules which marked the limits of the known world, blew a sailing vessel to the moon. For 7 days the raging storm carried the travellers through the air, and on the eighth day they landed on the moon, which floated ahead of them "like a shining island."

Johannes Kepler, who established the laws of planetary orbits, a great astronomer who knew through his studies that the earth's atmosphere could not reach to the moon, made his moon trip allegorical: the spirits of astronomy carry the astronomer to the moon across the shadow bridge which forms temporarily during an eclipse. The trip goes through airless space in his story and lasts only minutes—but Kepler too speaks of the "shining island of Levania" when referring to the moon.

We now have our own ideas of what a moon trip will be like. We know that it will begin with tense minutes of waiting on a mountain top near the equator, above the densest and most troublesome layers of the atmosphere. We know that finally there will be zero hour, zero minute, and zero second, and then the roaring bellow from the exhaust nozzles of the ship, sound ringing simultaneously through all registers of which sound is capable, accompanied by those dark subsonic vibrations which the human ear cannot hear but which cause those exposed to them to be afraid. We know that the ship will ride up on the roaring flames, disappearing in the sky in less than a minute. At first its path will be vertical, as usual, but then the ship's nose will be tilted eastward, because that way it can utilize the speed of the earth's rotation. Of course the moon will not be in line with the ship's nose. The ship will point to the spot where the moon is going to be 4 days later.

The slender ship, possibly equipped with wings which are to aid its landing after return, will leave the earth's atmosphere about 3 minutes after takeoff. But the rocket motors, for this trip, will have to work for about 8 minutes. This figure of 8 minutes has a special significance. It has not been selected for any theoretical reasons of high efficiency nor because of a formula saying this or that. It has been selected with regard to the pilot. Naturally the ship will be more efficient the faster it reaches a high velocity. But in changing

51

from one velocity to another acceleration is involved. And the pilot, who is incapable of feeling velocity per se, is quite sensitive to changes in velocity— to acceleration. The highest acceleration a normal healthy man can be expected to stand for several minutes is 4 g. Calculated with 4 g, the length of time required to reach escape velocity is close to 500 seconds or about 8 minutes.[1]

When the 8 minutes are up the ship will be far outside the earth's atmosphere. The earth will be a monstrous ball somewhere behind the ship, and the pilot will find himself surrounded by space. Black space, strewn all over with the countless jewels of distant suns, the stars. Stretching across the great blackness the pilot will see the Milky Way. The nearest star, our own sun, will shine with terrible incandescent brilliance on one side, its corona clearly visible as it was in the past only during total eclipses. But the distant stars will be visible in the immediate neighbourhood of the sun. The pilot will know, of course, that our sun, like all other stars, is really an atomic conversion furnace, and the formula which applies to the conversion going on in our sun, the so-called Solar Phoenix Reaction, will be as familiar to him as the fact that a rocket ship takes off vertically. Yet with all his modern knowledge, in spite of such abstractions as Keplerian ellipses in a gravitational field, the pilot will probably conceive of the moon as a great shining island in the black sky ahead of him—his goal.

During those 8 minutes of crushing acceleration the pilot may not be able to do much; in fact it is even possible that he may "black out" near the end of that period. Just because this possibility exists, the ship will be designed to take care of itself. The tilting mechanism, which will tilt the ship through an angle of 90 degrees during the period between $X+15$ seconds and $X+90$ seconds, will be fully automatic. The mechanism which cuts off the fuel supply when the calculated velocity has been reached will be fully automatic too.

Physically, the moment of *Brennschluss* may be quite a shock. For 8

---

[1] It may perhaps be useful to point out that the ship will not actually attain the full velocity of 7 miles per second. That velocity holds literally true only in the case of a cannon shot from the earth's surface; it would be somewhat less for a rocket ship attaining its maximum velocity some distance from the earth. What this figure of 7 miles per second actually represents is the amount of energy to be expended. If we call the energy required to lift a pound to a height of 1 foot a foot-pound, a 1-pound meteorite striking the earth at a velocity of 7 miles per second will have an energy of 46,232,000 foot-pounds. The ship has to have that energy for every pound of its weight.

minutes the muscles of the body have been straining under a 4 g acceleration. The breathing may have been slightly laboured (though by no means seriously so, as some have wanted to make out). And then, with fair suddenness, the acceleration will go down. It will not go down all at once—even in unmanned rockets the cut-off is in two stages, for various reasons. But it will go down fairly fast, and the important fact is that it does not go down from 4 g to the customary 1 g, but to zero. When the aggregate of cut-off mechanisms has done its work there will be no acceleration at all left. Only velocity. But the human body cannot feel velocity. The pilot will find himself weightless!

Second-rate novelists have made a great to-do about the pilot's finding himself surrounded by space on all sides. They have talked fearfully about the "psychical impact." In reality the pilot will probably need quite some time before he even gets around to observing this condition. The physical impact of rather sudden weightlessness—especially in contrast to the preceding period of acceleration—is much more important. But since quite similar conditions will be experienced during transcontinental jumps of winged rockets, this will not be a complete novelty to the pilot. What will be new to him is the duration of this apparent weightlessness. Under the conditions outlined it takes 4 days to go to the moon. It is interesting that a rather small velocity increase during the period of acceleration will reduce the duration of the trip to about 9 hours, and future generations will probably look back at those 4 days with the same attitude that we display toward the time when the crossing of the Atlantic Ocean took 4 weeks. They were he-men all right, but why did they waste all that time to prove it!

The 4 days will be difficult. Floating in the atmosphere of the cabin might be amusing for a while and quite comfortable for sleeping. But when it comes to doing any work it will be a nuisance—and eating a meal goes under the heading of "work" in a spaceship in "free flight." The apparent weightlessness is after all not restricted to the person of the pilot. It extends to everything that is not bolted, riveted, or welded to walls or floors. If the pilot reaches for a pencil and just touches it instead of gripping it, the pencil will sail away and bounce off a wall, unless the wall is padded. Incidentally, the pilot will have to use a pencil or a ball-point pen, since the ink in ordinary fountain pens flows out because of its weight. If the pilot tries to reach quickly for his elusive pencil he'll go sailing off himself, not necessarily in the same direction, or at least only approximately the same. His muscles are accustomed to moving his weight against 1 *g* at the earth's surface. Operating against 0 *g* they'll produce effects which everybody will think most humorous, except the victim.

Working during the "free" (meaning "unpowered") section of the trip will need some preparations. The shape they'll finally take will be derived from actual experience. At first it will simply be a matter of having everything tied down. Pencils, rulers, handbooks, and whatever small instruments are needed will be chained to the desk top, which probably would be hinged against the wall to be moved out of the way as a whole when not needed. The pilot's seat will have a safety belt like the one on the seat in an airplane. There will be strategically placed loops of nylon cord all over, since getting from one part of the cabin to another might be better accomplished by pulling than by pushing.

It may be remarked in passing that the bodily functions, including the swallowing of food, do not seem to depend on gravity at all, so that no trouble is to be expected from that quarter. But getting a meal ready might be a feat of agility. Of course one can slice bread or cheese, but one cannot pour anything. If the pilot succeeds in shaking a liquid out of its container it will form neat little globes by way of mutual attraction of the molecules and the globes will just hang suspended in the air. In fact this will be the most advantageous condition: you could then drink them by means of the drinking straw that should have been used in the first place. If the container is shaken too strongly the balls of liquid will hit a wall, break up into small balls which take off literally in all directions at once, and the final result will be a fine mist of droplets.

Trying to brush lint off a uniform must be something especially nice—but you can go on now and figure things out for yourself. I should mention that very slight gravitational effects exist even in a ship that moves "free"; slight effects caused by the mass of the heaviest parts of the ship itself, presumably the fuel tanks. Things floating around in the atmosphere of the cabin will have a slight tendency to collect on the floor, if the fuel tanks are located below the cabin, as is likely. But that will take time; they might be ready for collection from the floor after a sleeping period.

54

While the pilot will probably use a great deal of the time for astronomical observations, it should be emphasized that in his capacity as a pilot he will actually have very little work to do. After the period of acceleration he'll verify the ship's velocity and position and if necessary make a few small corrections. But after that, all the actual work of the 4 days could probably be done in 4 hours, in a very leisurely fashion. At about 215,000 miles from the earth (counting the centre of the planet as "earth") the ship will reach the point where the gravitational attractions of earth and moon balance each other. If everything has gone right the ship will pass that point, or line, with a very low velocity, a few feet per second. Now the ship must be turned so that the exhaust nozzle of the main motor points toward the moon. It could have been turned sooner, since the position of the ship's body on its line of movement is immaterial in space.

The landing itself will look very much like a take-off. The velocity imparted to the ship by the moon's gravity must be killed and that can be done only by rocket action, or rocket reaction, if you prefer that usage. The ship will be balanced down on her tail, the balancing manœuvre performed by the same mechanism that did the balancing during take-off. Again the pilot has very little to do with the landing. He will sit and watch his instruments, which tell him position, velocity, and deceleration of the ship, and, by means of bounced radar waves, its altitude above the lunar surface. But the actual work will be done by the preset instruments. The instant the ship touches, the motor will be cut off.

There will be a great silence.

The ship will have reached the shining island of Levania of which Kepler dreamed. And with that landing the third era of astronomy will begin.

It is interesting and perhaps significant that Kepler himself stood precisely at the turning point of the first two eras of astronomy. From the time when Babylonian astronomer-priests looked up to the lights in the sky to see the abodes and possibly to learn the will of their gods to the time of Kepler's own teacher Tycho Brahe the astronomer's main "instrument" had been his eyes. There were some astronomical instruments, simple devices for comparing and for measuring angles, but they did no more than establish a line of

55

sight properly. The astronomer's eye was not otherwise assisted and the astronomer with the better eyes had a great advantage. It was just the fact of "poor eyesight" (presumably a slight myopia) which caused Kepler to devote himself to the mathematical aspects of astronomy in which he made his great discoveries. He made them because he could not be a good observer. But during his lifetime the telescope was invented in the Netherlands and brought to quick fame by Galilei.

The second era of astronomy began, dominated by the *optical* instrument. And the optical instrument gradually added a new discipline to astronomy, that of exploring and describing the surfaces of the heavenly bodies. During the first, the naked-eye era, all astronomy had consisted of the knowledge and description of the apparent motions of these bodies. Nothing but the observation of these motions had been possible. Now the surfaces could be scrutinized.

This is true even for the moon. In fact it is surprisingly true just in the case of the moon. The naked eye can and does tell that there are lighter and darker patches and the imagination at once takes hold of this fact and produces strange mythological figures. Or, if the imagination be refined and controlled, it jumps to the conclusion that these may be land and sea. But a naked-eye view of the moon does no more than reveal the existence of lighter and darker areas. Not even their distribution is quite clear and definite. The picture changes at once if only a small amount of optical magnification is provided. Some five-diameters' magnification is all that is needed to make the picture of a different world stand out in detail. The first astronomers who had a few diameters of optical magnification at their disposal, complete with annoying if beautiful rainbow fringes, avidly went to work. There was a new world to be conquered, even if only optically, and every man who turned a lens-equipped tube toward the sky could feel himself a Columbus.

Maps of the moon were drawn and peppered over with names, useful for the identification of landmarks but sadly misleading because of their terrestrializing connotations. The moon is not merely a smaller earth, as some of the ancient Greek philosophers phrased it, it is a different world with a "style" all its own. Both similarities and differences of appearance have to be treated with caution. We now distinguish five major types of topographical features on the moon: *maria*, mountain chains, "craters," "rills," and "rays,"

56

and at least three of these five types of surface features are mysterious.

Because they are the largest, and darker to the eye than the lunar landscape in general, the *maria* were discovered first. Even with a weak and primitive telescope one could see at first glance that the moon presented a generally mountainous landscape, but that these mountainous areas either enclosed or were enclosed by large smooth areas, dark in colour. Obviously the flat areas were seas, *maria* in Latin. (The form *maria* is plural; the singular is *mare*. In both the accent is on the first syllable: *má-re* and *má-ria*.) They all received beautiful names, still printed on lunar maps. There is a Cloudy Sea (*Mare nubium*) and a Serene Sea (*Mare serenitatis*); there is a Stormy Ocean (*Oceanus procellarum*), and even a Misty Swamp (*Palus nebularum*). That one should look for a bay where there are seas is understandable, but why it should have been named Rainbow Bay (*Sinus iridum*) is less clear.

The second obvious feature was mountain chains, looking very much like those we have on earth. Johannes Hevelius of Danzig, who published a map of the moon in 1645, introduced the custom of labelling them with the names of terrestrial mountain chains, presumably to emphasize the similarity. Because of Hevelius the Sea of Showers (*Mare imbrium*) is bordered by the "Alps," the "Apennines," and the "Caucasus."

While the *maria* and the mountain chains compared (or seemed to compare) directly with their terrestrial counterparts, a third type of lunar formation, the most common of all, presented a puzzle. Wherever astronomers looked with their new enlarging instruments they saw "circular mountains," round structures now commonly called "craters." It is not a good name; the term "ringwall" which German astronomers have tried from time to time to introduce is much better because of its lack of connotations. Unfortunately it has failed to take hold.

First man to see these "craters" and also the first to draw a map of the moon was Galileo Galilei. He compared them in appearance with "the eyes on the tail feathers of a peacock." Naturally Galilei could see only the largest and most conspicuous of these formations. A chart published during the nineteenth century showed about 33,000 of them, and present estimates of the total number vary with the resolving power of the telescope used. As may be expected from these remarks, the "craters" come in all sizes. The largest, also called "walled plains" measure more than 150 miles across. Two fine examples of these have been named Clavious and Schickard. The best-known "craters," like Copernicus, Kepler, Plato, and Theophilus, have diameters on the order of 50 to 60 miles. But a great many smaller craters only 10 to 20 miles in diameter have been named too. The smaller varieties are called "craterlets," and finally "beads," the latter being only a few hundred yards across.

"Craters" are named after people—philosophers, scientists, and (mainly) astronomers, ancient and modern, well known and unknown. The custom was begun by one Langrenus of Brussels who was attached to the Spanish Court from 1620 to 1640 and found time to make a number of detailed drawings of some lunar formations. Hevelius, who came a few years later, knew of Langrenus's suggestion, but preferred geographical names taken from terrestrial objects. But the next lunar mapmaker, Riccioli of Bologna, enthusiastically adopted Langrenus's idea of naming craters after famous people.

Riccioli did not just scatter names over the map, but proceeded, one might say, by logic and by prejudice. Being an ardent admirer of Tycho Brahe, he picked the most conspicuous crater, just visible even to the naked eye when the moon is about full, provided you know where to look for it, and named it Tycho. Copernicus had assigned to him what is probably the most beautiful and most typical lunar crater. It is quite a distance from Tycho because Tycho Brahe's and Nicholas Copernicus's ideas about the shape of the solar system were quite different. Kepler, who agreed with Copernicus, was given a crater not far from Copernicus. Plato was honoured with a large and conspicuous crater on the northern hemisphere of the moon—the other large craters in that general area were called Aristotle, Timaeus, Eudoxus, Thales, Strabo, Pythagoras, and Epigenes, so to speak a "classical corner."

Many of Riccioli's names have become permanent; a few failed to survive, mainly because later astronomers were not quite sure which formation was meant. Since then the map has been filled in with countless other names: Gauss, Struve, Newton, Scheiner, Hevelius, and Mercator have their craters. Among people who to my knowledge did not contribute anything to astronomy but who got their craters anyway are Cavendish, Vasco da Gama, Réaumur, Lavoisier, Otto von Guericke, Darwin, and Wilhelm I. There is a crater named Benjamin Franklin, one named Fra Mauro, one named Henry Draper, and one named Mary Proctor. There is even a crater named Hell—named, it should be explained, after Father Maximilian Hell, S.J., who was once director of the Vienna Observatory.

The fourth type of feature is strange deep chasms which are usually referred to as "rills," an adaption of the German appellation *Rille*, which means "groove." They are never very wide but often quite long, and they confront theorists with the annoying fact that their courses seem to have nothing at all to do with the topography of the region in which they happen to be. They traverse mountains and *maria*, pass near and sometimes through small craters, and make in general about as much sense as a stroke with a blue pencil across a poster.

Fifth and finally, there are the "rays," long streaks of (by contrast) startling brightness, not very wide but up to a hundred miles in length. The "rays" pass over what should be obstacles as impartially and as casually as do the rills, but they always originate from a crater. The most conspicuous system of rays is that springing from the crater Tycho; in fact this is what makes Tycho so obvious that even the naked eye can make it out. The craters Copernicus and Kepler have similar systems. All three ray systems resemble the spokes of a wheel with the crater as the hub. But the crater Messier shows just two rays which run parallel across the dark plain of the *Mare foecunditatis* and which look strikingly like the twin beams of a double searchlight, indicating a safe passage in an otherwise dangerous sea.

Among the things which everybody knows about the moon are that it always points the same side to the earth and that it is without atmosphere. The first of these two facts is ancient knowledge, since it can be established by naked-eye observation. Aristotle is known to have deduced it, but it may have been Babylonian knowledge before him. The second fact could not be known until after the invention of the telescope. It is an interesting historical sidelight that during Aristotle's lifetime it happened that the disk of the moon appeared to pass over the planet Mars. To Aristotle this "occultation" (as such a performance is called by astronomers) proved the obvious: that the moon is nearer to the earth than Mars is. A modern astronomer could also use it to establish the airlessness of the moon.

Once the motions of both bodies are well known it is possible to calculate at what instant the moon's disk should begin to pass over the planet and also at what instant the planet should begin to reappear. If calculation and observation agree perfectly it proves that the moon has no air. For if it had air, the rays from Mars would be bent in this air and we should see Mars a little longer before it disappears and see it reappear a little earlier. But calculation and observation do agree, and this phenomenon has been checked over and over again during occultations of stars.

The modern astronomer, or rather his helper from the Department of Physics, also knows why the moon is airless, in fact he can prove that it was "always" without air. This means that the moon, if it once had an atmosphere, was not able to keep it more than a few thousand years at the most, unless gas wells and active volcanoes replaced the loss steadily for a while. The proof of this hinges on the velocity of liberation.

The molecules of a gas are in constant motion, and the velocity of that motion depends on two things only: the nature of the gas and the temperature. During the middle of its 2-week day the surface of the moon is heated by the sun to a temperature about one and a half times that of boiling water. At that temperature range the average velocity of a hydrogen molecule is about 1500 feet greater than the moon's escape velocity. Therefore the gravitational grip of the moon is too weak to hold hydrogen molecules. The same goes for helium molecules. For heavier gases like oxygen and nitrogen, the average velocity of the molecules is somewhat less than the moon's escape velocity, but that still does not mean that the moon can keep these gases. There is that little word "average" in front of the word velocity. The figures which the physicist calculates and writes down in table are averages—like the statement that the average woman is 5 feet 4 inches tall. Statistically this is correct, but there are many individual variations. Many oxygen and nitrogen molecules are faster than the average and these the moon could not hold. It could hold only those which happened to be average or slower. But during the next day there is again a set with a molecular velocity above average. And during the day after that . . .

The realization that the moon must have lost its atmosphere quickly—although it presumably had a gaseous envelope for some time during the early days of its career—led to Simon Newcomb's famous statement that the moon is a world without weather on which nothing ever happens. Newcomb may not have meant it literally, and it is not literally true. There is a strange kind of "weather" on the moon, caused by the same factors which removed the weather we know, the weather caused by air and moisture.

The temperature range on the moon, from lunar midday to lunar midnight, amounts to almost 600 degrees Fahrenheit. Rocks exposed to such temperature changes at regular 2-week intervals will crack. Their crystalline structure will give way under repeated expansion and contraction and the surface will flake off. The result should be that the moon's surface be covered with fine rock dust. Since there is no wind to move it around, the rock dust will leave the place where it formed only because of gravity. The peaks, therefore, will be exposed to the sun and to further disintegration, while the amount of dust accumulated at the less steep slopes may be considerable. In general, however, the layer of rock dust is likely to be quite shallow, since a dust layer, once formed, will insulate the solid rock underneath. Incidentally the brightness of the moon and a few other factors support the assumption that the sun's light is reflected by pulverized basalt or similar rocks.

During Kepler's lifetime the second era of astronomy had not yet progressed far enough to establish the lack of an atmosphere on the moon as a certainty. Kepler could still believe in air on the moon and in inhabitants of the moon. In fact he needed that hypothesis in order to explain the "craters." He took them to be artificial structures, circular walls erected by the selenites (inhabitants of the moon) as a safeguard against the swampiness of the *maria* and also against the rays of the sun. Hevelius, on the other hand, was already sure that the moon was essentially airless, but he believed that it might be inhabited just the same. Hevelius also knew that the *maria* were not seas, and probably not even swamps, as Kepler seems to have thought.

It must have been hard to give up the belief in selenites. The telescope had showed that the moon actually was a world with mountains and valleys and large plains—but the same telescope showed that it had no noticeable body of water and no atmosphere. No matter how much it hurt, one could not do anything against facts. But it is also understandable that some astronomers did not bury their hopes completely. If you wanted to believe in selenites there were still two possibilities. One was to believe in extinct selenites and to look for traces of their works. The other was to take advantage of the fact that the moon has its "unknown hemisphere," the side we never see.

Both were tried.

During the late evening hours of the twelfth of July, 1822, a Munich astronomer, Franz von Paula Gruithuisen, examined an area close to the centre of the visible half of the moon. There is a rill in that area, usually called the Hyginus rill because it runs through the crater Hyginus in the southern portion of the *Mare vaporum*. Near the Hyginus rill there is a formation which on German maps is marked *Schneckenberg* (Snail Mountain) because it resembles the upper portion of an enormous snail half covered by mud or tar. The whole area in fact gives such an impression: at some distance there are mountains which look as if they might be the upper ridges and peaks of ranges whose lower portions had been buried in a viscous liquid that later hardened. The formation as a whole looks strange enough to seem artificial. Gruithuisen did not hesitate to say that it was artificial. He took it to be the ruins of an old fortress that had once guarded a city.

After an interval of breathlessness which followed Gruithuisen's announcement, other observers, especially Gruithuisen's compatriot Mädler, tried to discredit the "fortress of the selenites." Gruithuisen had published a drawing of the spot. Mädler did too. Gruithuisen had drawn the ruins of a fortress and a city. Mädler drew an irregular pattern of mountain ridges crossing one another. In fairness one must say that each exaggerated in the direction of what he wanted to prove. The formations are by no means as regular and "convincing" as Gruithuisen showed them. Nor is the landscape as featureless as Mädler drew it. In the telescope it simply fails to make sense. The final word will have to be spoken in the third era of astronomy when an explorer can stand at the foot of Snail Mountain and look at the formation through the transparent plastic of his air helmet.

The man who wanted to move the selenites to the other side of the moon was Peter Andreas Hansen. He was a Danish watchmaker, a term which then also covered what we would call a precision mechanic today. Hansen obtained a job as an assistant surveyor in the Danish Survey, somehow became associated with the then new observatory at Altona, and proved his ability as an astronomer. In 1825 he was called to the famous University of Gotha as director of the Seeberg Observatory and began to distinguish himself by his theoretical work. His paper on the mutual perturbations of Jupiter and Saturn won a prize from the Berlin Academy. His paper on the orbits of comets won a prize from the Paris Academy. His Tables of Lunar Motions were published at the expense of the British government and incorporated in the Nautical Almanac. The Royal Astronomical Society awarded him a gold medal. The Royal Academy of Sciences of Saxony made a standing offer to publish all his works. In short, Hansen was a man of international fame, a fame founded not on any accidental discovery, but on solid and hard work and large amounts of it.

Small wonder that everybody listened attentively when Hansen announced that the prevailing conceptions about the moon should be revised. He began by affirming the known facts: the boiling temperature on the silent plains of the *maria*, the bleak mountain ridges rearing into an airless black sky, the large craters devoid of any activity. But, he said, the sum total of what we do see is the result of something we don't see—the fact that the moon is not a sphere. Certain peculiarities of the moon's motion indicate that it is not spherical but roughly egg-shaped. The narrow end of this egg-shaped world is pointing towards the earth. What we see is this narrow end, rising like an enormous mountain over the ideal but nonexistent sphere which we thought the moon to be. Of course there is no air on top of this gigantic mountain because it extends above the lunar atmosphere. All water that exists on the moon must have flowed off that mountain and assembled in larger and smaller bodies on the other hemisphere. And the other hemisphere, if it is permissible to use this term with reference to a nonspherical body, does not rise above the atmosphere. It has an atmosphere and water, and where there are water and air there is vegetation, and where there is vegetation there are animals—and among the animals there are possibly thinking beings, selenites.

It would have been a wonderful idea if it had originated with the butler of the third assistant secretary to the Duke of Schlobenstein-Donnerwetter. That it originated with Herr Professor Peter Andreas Hansen made it all the more wonderful. This was far superior in every respect to Gruithuisen's abandoned fortress. The pity was that we would never be able to see this world. But while everybody was impressed, the astronomers began to look for a weak link in the argument. They found it in the fundamental assumption. Certain peculiarities in the motion of the moon had caused the assumption that the moon was not spherical. One had to look at those peculiarities.

The orbit of the moon happens to present one of the most difficult problems of mathematical astronomy. Partly because it was so difficult (and therefore intriguing), a great amount of work had already been done on it in Hansen's time. Because of Hansen the problem was attacked once more, with even greater care and thoroughness, backed by new and more precise observations and by new mathematical methods. Finally Simon Newcomb succeeded in proving that the moon is at least as spherical as the earth.

Hansen's supermountain simply does not exist. It was a fine fantasy but it had unfortunately nothing to do with reality.

Because of Hansen a German observatory inaugurated a special study of "the other side." Such a study can be made to some extent even without spaceships. The moon turns on its axis once during the interval of time it takes to go once around the earth. The result of the combination of these two motions is that we always look at the same hemisphere. And if the moon's orbit were circular we would see precisely 50 per cent of its surface, some of this area, near the rim, ill defined. But the moon's orbit is elliptical, its motion faster when it is nearer earth and slower farther away. The irregular motion combined with the regular rotation produces a kind of "wobble" which enables us to see temporarily portions "beyond the rim," once on one side and once on the other. Taking advantage of the libration, as the wobble is called in dignified professional language, we can map a total of about four-sevenths of the lunar surface. That special study proved that Newcomb was right and not Hansen. Some *mare* plains continue across the rim and a few large but typical craters appear from time to time. The "other side" is no different from the one we see.

But what is it we see?

There are still a few old "popular lecturers" around who will tell their audiences with perfectly straight faces that the *maria* are ancient sea bottoms, that the rills are old river beds of the type of the Grand Canyon, and that the craters are extinct volcanoes. The picture they try to draw is that of a smaller earth which aged more rapidly and long ago lost its watery oceans and its air ocean. While I can quote the titles and authors of the books from which they derived their misinformation half a century or so ago, I can't quite see how anybody can pass on things like that for decades without once thinking about them.

For example: how would the bottom of the Atlantic Ocean look if all the water evaporated out of it? To begin with, it would be blinding white because of the salt left behind. And the chances are overwhelming that the seas of the moon, if ever it had any, would have been salty too. Even without the salt the picture would be different: the bottoms of our oceans are not just flat basins, they are mountainous in spots, with deep depressions elsewhere; in short, their topography is such that, emptied and without salt, they could scarcely be distinguished from "land" when seen from the moon. But the *maria* are large smooth plains with hardly any topographical variety except for an occasional new-looking "crater" or a rill, of virtually uniform darkish colour. They are not even far below the general level of the moon, completely lacking the "deeps" of terrestrial seas.

The canyons on earth are straight for only short stretches. They wind their way through the landscape, as do the courses of ordinary rivers. They avoid mountains and very often have mountains sticking up from their floors, to the height of the surrounding plateau. The rills are much straighter and their courses pay no attention to other topographical features. They carelessly cut through mountains and are themselves occasionally cut short by craters.

As regards the "rays," there are no similar formations on earth, to the best of our knowledge, although they might show up if seen from some distance in space. Such a possibility exists; aviators can often see varied shades of green in the vegetation of an area caused by different minerals in the ground, where on the ground this difference is too small to be observed.

As for the craters, one is led to suspect that much of the discussion about them is due to semantic compulsion: some time in the past some dunderhead thought that the word "crater" would be a nice convenient name for the lunar ringwalls and ever since a number of additional dunderheads have tried to prove that the things called "craters" actually *are* craters.

The vast majority of lunar craters show no resemblance whatever to a volcanic crater, although a number of the tiny "beads" might actually be of volcanic origin. A volcanic crater is a hole on top of a mountain. The hole is

65

considerably above the level of the surrounding territory. The outer slopes of the mountain are marked with lava flows. In fact the whole cone is built up of lava flows. The interior of the crater, when inactive, is funnel-shaped but irregular. The outline of the crater hole is usually irregular too, and our largest craters happen to have the most irregular outlines. Old inactive craters that have weathered down rarely present full circles. What is left after the weathering shows about the same slope on the inside as it does on the outside. If there is a young crater in or on an old eroded crater it is always considerably higher than the old crater. And the interior of the old crater is considerably above the surrounding territory. The diameter of the largest active crater known is about 1 mile; the largest eroded crater rim known is about 10 miles in diameter. Volcanoes are arranged along weak lines in the earth's crust.

And the lunar ringwalls?

Their arrangement is completely random. In mapping them, no lines of weakness, in fact no lines at all, could be found. The most typical objects have diameters ranging from 15 to 120 miles. The ringwall is always a complete and rather regular circle. Naturally the ones near the rim of the moon look elliptical to us, but they are actually circles too. A few lunar ringwalls are actually elliptical, but they are as regular ellipses as the majority are regular circles. The slope of the ringwalls is always more gentle on the outside than on the inside, though some have generally steeper slopes than others. But the inner slope is always steeper than the outer. The floor in every ringwall is always *below* the general level of the surrounding territory and in large ringwalls can be seen to conform to the curvature of the moon, at a lower level. Not quite 50 per cent of all ringwalls have a central peak, the others don't. If there is no central peak, the floor is smooth, not of that puzzling smoothness of the *maria* but nonetheless smooth. If there is a central peak it is always in the precise centre of the otherwise smooth floor of the circular ringwall, and it always attains about the level of the surrounding territory but never the level of the peaks of the ringwall. If either the ringwall itself or its floor shows a major interruption it is caused by a smaller ringwall of the same type. And in most cases the volume of the ringwall is just about what would be needed to fill the depression.

It is not even necessary to mention that there are no lava flows. The picture presented by a lunar ringwall is most decidedly not that of a volcano.

66

In fact volcanism could not account for a single one of the features just described. And this picture is repeated over and over again, thirty-three thousand times.

The first astronomer to guess at the true origin of these craters was, of all people, old Gruithuisen. At one point in his writing he mentioned, quite casually, that the lunar craters looked like impact craters caused by cosmic matter. A decade or so later an engineer named Althans arrived at the same conclusion. It is not likely that Althans had ever read Gruithuisen's writings, but he had taken part in the well-known life struggle of ordnance engineers, the struggle to devise an armour plate which cannot be pierced by any projectile and then to design a gun which can pierce that armour plate. Watching this going on, he was struck by the similarity of shot holes in tough armour plate to the craters on the moon. Althans even experimented a bit, using balls of grapeshot for meteorites and pans filled with fresh mortar for a surface.

The first well-known astronomer who accepted the impact theory—I don't know whether he knew of Althans' experiments or not—was Sir Richard A. Proctor in 1873, and since then the "meteorite impact party" has grown steadily. The discovery of Meteor Crater in Arizona proved decisive to many people. There was a mile-wide crater on earth, formed in solid rock, but most decidedly not volcanic in origin. This crater showed gentle slopes on the outside and steep slopes on the inside. Its floor was below general surface level and smooth. Tons of meteorite fragments were collected from its rim and surroundings. There was no doubt, after examination, that it had been formed instantly by the impact of a very large meteorite, though at first geologists had thought it the result of a volcanic steam explosion, and there was also no doubt that its proportions agreed with those of lunar ringwalls (Fig. 5). Later it was found that Meteor Crater in Arizona was not unique on earth. Many other such craters are now more or less well known, but this one is still the largest and in many respects the most typical.

All this was very gratifying indeed. Impact craters did not have to adhere to lines of weakness, they could score hits in the middle of *maria*, they could partly obliterate another old impact crater, they could score direct hits on older ringwalls—in short they could account for everything that the volcanic theory could not possibly explain. But there was some doubt left about the mechanism of ringwall formation. On earth, because there is water in the ground, one could have made out a case for a steam explosion. For the moon this idea would not do. How did it work then without water?

The answer was provided in 1918 by a geologist, Dr. Alfred Wegener, who is chiefly known among geologists as the originator of the theory of "continental drift." Doctor Wegener started out by thinking about the natural forces involved in such an impact. In general there are two kinds of forces, molecular forces (strength of material) and mass forces (gravitation). Both are present in any impact or collision, but their ratio depends on its magnitude. In all small-scale impacts the presence of molecular forces is important—when, for example, you drop a stone in mud—but when it comes to the crash of a meteorite weighing 20 tons or more with an impact velocity of 10 miles or higher per second, the strength of the meteorite or of the surface which it hits is unimportant. In such a crash any material would be smashed, whether it be soft pumice or alloy steel. Therefore, if you want to simulate a meteorite crash in the laboratory you have to use a material which has *no tensile strength*.

There is such a material: it is dust. Doctor Wegener for practical reasons used cement dust: it comes in uniform quality; and the results of the experiments can afterwards be hardened by spraying with water. The experiment is so simple that it can be performed anywhere where the accompanying mess does no harm. The surface is prepared by putting a layer of cement powder in a shallow pan. The meteorite is a spoonful of the same powder, dropped from a height of about 4 feet. The results are amazing: craters which not only look like moon craters but also show the same proportions. And the average of twenty such "craters" which were hardened and then measured carefully agreed beautifully with the proportions of Meteor Crater. In a few cases the falling mass separated before it struck and created a twin crater of precisely the appearance of those known to astronomers.

After the basic procedure had been found to work, the problem of "what happens to the meteorite?" was attacked. In this experiment a plaster of Paris "meteorite" was used. The result was a surprise. The whole "crater" (which in the experiments usually has four times the diameter of the falling mass) was white. A cross section showed that the "meteoric matter" was thinnest over the crater floor and somewhat concentrated on the inner rim of the ringwall.

A good deal splashed over the rim—in my own experiments I found particles more than a yard from the centre of the 4-inch crater. There was no "main mass" and it is probably significant that no main mass could be found under the Arizona crater although much meteoric matter was scattered for many miles around the crater rim.

The central peak was the next problem which did not admit of immediate answer. Then it was solved accidentally. In the laboratory experiment one obtains a crater with a central peak only if the layer of cement is rather thin, less than an inch deep. This probably means that a central peak formed on the moon in those places where a relatively thin layer of surface rock is backed by thick layers of heavy rock. Repetition of the accidental experiment that resulted in a central peak of plaster of Paris, and subsequent cross sectioning, showed that the central peak was simply undisturbed ground matter, possibly

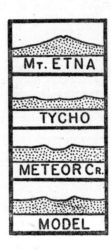

FIG. 5. Crater profiles. Top, typical terrestrial volcano, Mount Etna; then Mount Tycho on the moon, Meteor Crater in Arizona, and, bottom, typical model produced as described on pages 68 and 69.

crushed and deformed, but left in place. Logically the central peak is always lower than the crater rim, since the rim is ground material piled high.

The *maria* differ from the largest craters, the walled plains, in only two respects. One is their size; the other is their smoothness (disturbed only by additional impact craters, few in number). Presumably the *maria* were formed by meteorites large enough to break through the crust of the moon and cause liquid magma from the interior to well up. *Mare crisium* is a fine example, as a quick glance at any lunar photograph will show. So is the still larger *Mare imbrium*—one can clearly see around its rim that some areas were only partly flooded by the molten rock. And in some *maria*, especially *Mare imbrium*, one can see so-called "vein mountains," older mountains which were melted down but did not disappear completely.

As for the rills, obviously younger than everything else, they might be just cracks. But we cannot examine them by telescope and no decision will be possible until we get to the moon. The rays are also unexplained, but since we know that they never produce shadows they can be neither elevations nor depressions.

It has been suggested that the craters with rays were made by iron meteorites and that the rays themselves are splashes of droplets of vaporized metal. These metallic droplets and flakes would show against the background of rock and rock dust, while similar splashes made by the impact of stony meteorites would not. In case this explanation is correct, Meteor Crater in Arizona might have a system of rays, invisible to us and probably obliterated by weather during the 6000 to 10,000 years that have passed since its origin.

Full moon is not the best time for observing. When the sun rises or sets over the lunar landscape, the rims of the ringwalls cast long shadows which betray their shape. But when the moon is full to us and the sun stands vertically over *maria* and mountains, everything looks flat and only differences of colour show in a virtually featureless picture. However, on the moon's northern hemisphere, in that "classical corner," there is the large crater of Plato. Sunrise over Plato is just like sunrise over any other crater. But as the dividing line between darkness and light, the terminator, advances, the floor of Plato grows darker. At high noon it looks like an inkspot.

What happens in the crater of Plato? Evaporation of moisture forming a light-absorbing mist? Or just melting ice? Or crystals with freakish optical qualities?

The mystery of Plato has recently deepened further, because the most active group of planetary observers today, headed by W. H. Haas, contradicts the by now almost traditional assertion that Plato looks grey at lunar sunrise and black at lunar noon. It is highly unlikely that all the older observers have been wrong; after all they were not talking about a minor detail but about a very conspicuous feature. It is equally unlikely that the modern observers are mistaken. One has to conclude, therefore, that a change of some kind has taken place.[1]

Just what is going on there, or has been going on, is a question which the second era of astronomy, the telescopic era, cannot answer. The answer will have to wait for the third era with its spaceships.

Some 70 miles west of Plato, in the middle of the "Alps," there is the Great Valley (plate xx), about 90 miles long and up to 6½ miles wide. It runs almost at right angles to the few and very small other valleys of the "Alps." Its floor is smooth, to the best of observational evidence. And we have no explanation for it at all. One might think of a meteorite some 6 miles in diameter grazing the moon and ploughing through the mountains, except that the valley, while straight, does not seem quite straight enough for such an explanation. And why is its floor smooth?

We'll never know until we get there.

Then there is, of course, Gruithuisen's old puzzle of the "lunar fortress" to be solved. And the problem of the bright surface of the crater Aristarchus (plate xviiia), which looks just like the plaster of Paris craters Dr. Wegener made in his laboratory. There are Professor William H. Pickering's observations. He thinks he saw a snowstorm on Mount Pico (plate xxiib) which would indicate something like a thin temporary atmosphere in that vicinity. South of the *Mare imbrium* in which Pico is situated there is the crater Eratosthenes. If it were not for Pickering, Eratosthenes would simply be regarded as a medium-sized, very typical, and very beautiful crater. But Pickering repeatedly observed greyish spots moving around inside the crater. Cloud formations betraying the presence of moisture? Or lunar vegetation springing up and being killed off by the heat of the sun in a rapid cycle?

We'll never know until we get there.

Near the rim of the moon there is the crater Wargentin. It too would be a normal crater in every respect if it were not for the fact that it is full. The crater is literally brimful. And flat. The colour is about the same as elsewhere, as far as one can observe, but observation is difficult in this case because

[1] W. H. Haas prepared a list of twenty-two changes on the moon found during 1,000 hours of observing time which he is convinced are real and which he tentatively attributes to vegetation.

the crater is near the rim. Did a meteorite break through the crust? Did this form the crater or was there a later impact in an existing crater? The latter seems more likely: it is hard to imagine that a meteorite that broke through the crust could simultaneously produce a typical crater.

Then there is the great "walled plain" of Clavius, well over 150 miles across. Since it was formed seven smaller meteorites have scored hits on its ringwall, and there are four major and half a dozen minor impact craters in its interior. Obviously they are younger than Clavius since they are super-imposed upon it. But they also look younger. The old walls look as if they had been subjected to erosion. This is true for a few other walled plains too. What kind of erosion?

And finally we have the mystery of Linné, a crater named after Karl von Linné (known in this country under the Latinized version of his name, Linnaeus) and situated in the *Mare serenitatis*. Linné shows up against the dark *mare* plain as a whitish spot, looking alike through the whole lunar day, too low to cast a noticeable shadow. A few astronomers beginning in about 1890 claimed that, under exceptional seeing conditions and with a big instrument, a tiny hole could be discerned in the centre of the white spot. But Schmidt, in 1843, described Linné as a crater some 6 miles across and an estimated 1200 feet deep. He and several other astronomers of his period used Linné as a landmark in the otherwise smooth *mare* plain, a reference point for measurements. Nobody would use it now for this purpose, even though it stands alone on the *mare* plain, nor is Schmidt's description even remotely correct. But neither does there seem any chance for a mistake, since Linné does stand isolated and the position of the white spot of today agrees with the position given in 1843.

Is Linné a real volcano that was active some time between 1860 and 1890?

Some day we'll be able to find out, a few years after the first spaceship lands on the moon.

IX. "Zero hour minus five"—preparing the ship for its trip to the moon.

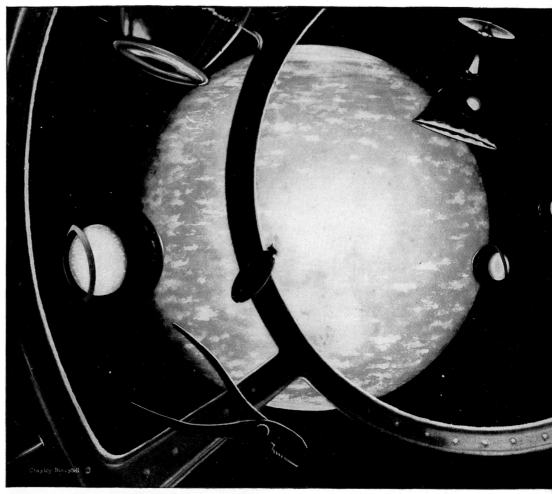

X*a*. Fifteen thousand miles out from the earth, coasting without power. Utensils have no apparent weight and liquids released from their containers form spheres.

X*b*. Thirty-five thousand miles out. Down there at the west coast of North America, the sun is setting. In the ship there is neither night nor day.

XI. Forty-five hundred miles from the moon, one-half of which is brilliantly illuminated by the sun, while the other half lies in faint earthlight. At this distance the ship is in the gravitational field of the moon and indeed is falling towards the moon. It will soon be necessary to activate the rocket motors in order to slow the fall, but all the necessary braking can be accomplished in as little as 150 seconds.

XII. One of the most impressive mountain ranges on the moon, the Leibnitz Mountains, which Camille Flammarion called "the mountains of eternal light." They are 30,000 feet high, probably surpassing the highest mountain ranges on earth. They are pictured during an eclipse of the sun by the earth.

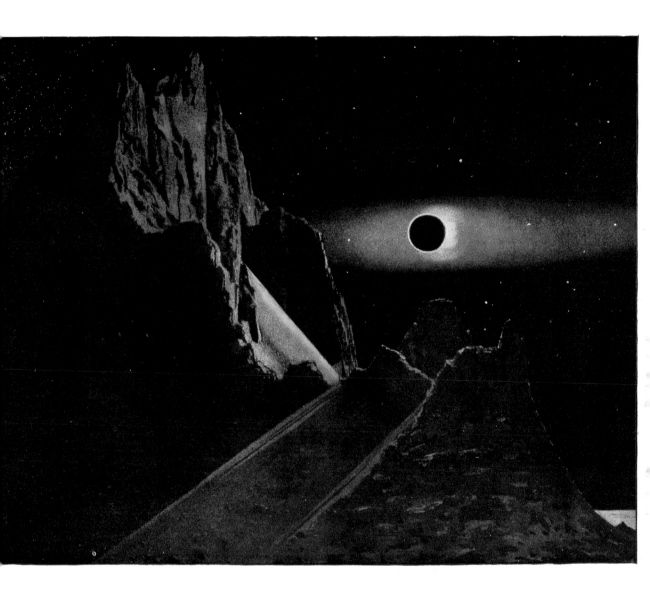

XIII. An eclipse of the sun by the earth. Seen from the earth, both the sun and the moon happen to appear of nearly equal size, about $\frac{1}{2}$ degree of arc. Seen from the moon, the sun is still the same apparent size, since the distance between the earth and the moon is negligible compared to the distance between the earth (or the moon) and the sun. But as the earth is a much larger body than the moon, its disc, seen from the moon, has four times the apparent diameter of that of the sun. Therefore an eclipse of the sun will last much longer. The sun's rays are refracted through the earth's atmosphere; the moon is illuminated by red light passing through.

77

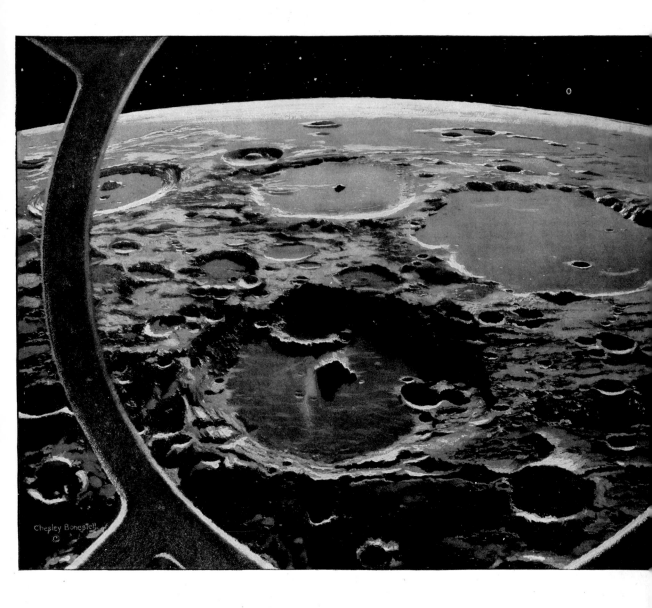

XIV. Two hundred miles above the moon, over the centre of the disc as we see it from earth. The larger crater in the centre is 80-mile-wide Albategnius; the other three large craters are Ptolemaeus (90 miles), Alphonsus (65 miles), and Arzachel (60 miles). While these four large craters were formed by the same cause, it is evident that they are not of the same age. Albategnius looks as if it were younger than the others.

XV*a*. Fifty miles above the moon. The large crater is Theophilus, 64 miles in diameter. Compare for scale with picture below.

XV*b*. Fifty miles above San Francisco Bay. This picture and the one above show areas of equal size and the visual angle is 40 degrees in each.

XVI. Beginnings of the lunar base; the weekly transport to earth, which illuminates the landscape, is being readied. The distant mountains are already illuminated by the rising sun.

80

XVII. One of the most interesting features on the moon, the Great Wall, also called the "Railway," which is 60 to 75 miles long and except for one end perfectly straight. It must be a gigantic fault, larger than any known on earth (especially if we think of *straight* faults) and ranges from 500 to 1500 feet in height. Double shadows in foreground are caused by earthlight.

XVIII*a*. The crater Aristarchus, 29 miles in diameter, the brightest spot on the moon (white pumice?). The other crater is Herodotus. The canyon is Schroeter's canyon. Ship is 30 miles above the moon's surface.

XVIII*b*. Promontory Laplace in foreground, promontory Heraclides on horizon. The "bay" is *Sinus iridum*. The mountains are 15,000 to 20,000 feet high. Ship is 10 miles above the moon's surface.

XIX. A study in apparent sizes. The constellation Orion and the earth over a lunar valley. Orion's belt is 3 degrees wide, the earth in the lunar sky about 2 degrees. Valley shows signs "thermal erosion" (*see* chapter 2).

XX. The Great Valley of the "Alps," seen from a ship 10 miles above the moon. The valley is illuminated by earthlight which must be about sixty times as bright as "full moon" is to us. (One should be able to read in earthlight without too much eyestrain.) The sun is setting behind the lonely mountain Pico.

XXI. The ship is circling the moon some 10 miles above its surface and is now over the lunar pole. The lunar landscape looks the same at the pole as elsewhere. The earth now touches the lunar horizon and will soon have disappeared from view. Seen from the moon the earth has an apparent diameter of about 2 degrees, which means that it appears four times as large as the moon does to us.

85

XXII*a*. Standing on a high peak on the eastern wall of the crater Copernicus, looking west at the afternoon sun. Copernicus is probably the most beautiful of all lunar craters. Its ringwall is 12,000 feet high at the highest point; its diameter is 56 miles.

XXII*b*. Ship is 25 miles over Mount Pico which is 10,000 feet high. The large crater in the distance is Plato; the other isolated mountains have been named the Tenerife Mountains.

Chesley B. ...onell ☽

XXIII. View from the rim of the crater Theophilus into its interior. The central peaks are 8,000 feet high, the opposite rim 16,000 to 18,000 feet high, and 64 miles away. Double shadows are caused by earthlight; for all the areas of the moon which we can see from earth, the earth never sets.

XXIV. The ship, having landed on its tail, will take off from this position for the return to earth.

3. THE SOLAR FAMILY

THE STORY has come down to us from the late Middle Ages that one of the kings of Spain, after listening to a long lecture by his court astrologer about the construction of the world, remarked that if the Lord and Creator had asked his advice he would have made it less complicated.

The remark referred, of course, to what is now called the Ptolemaic system, after Claudius Ptolemaeus—although it was actually invented by Hipparchus the Greek who also compiled the first star catalogue. Hipparchus had very simply and modestly assumed that the earth was the centre of the universe and that everything else had to revolve around it. Now the trouble with most philosophical ideas is that they have fragile frames and sensitive skins, while facts have sharp corners. The positions of those "stars" which the Greeks called *planetes* (wanderers) because they do not stay in one place should have supported that assumption. They did so only if you admitted that they did not describe a circle around the earth, but that each of them ran on a small circle the centre of which described a larger circle around the earth.

That assumption worked for a while but as the number of observations increased it was found to be not *quite* right. However, there was still a way out. While the earth was obviously, naturally, and indubitably the centre of the universe, it so happened that the centres of the large circles did not coincide with the centre of the earth. That again seemed to work for a while, but then it was found that one had to introduce irregular movement too: either the planets did not run with constant speed on their epicycles (the assumed small circles) or else the centres of the epicycles did not move with constant speed along the larger circles. It was at this point that the king of Spain made his observation—not strictly an astronomical one.

Soon after this, Nicholas Copernicus of Thorn turned the picture upside down. To him the planets still ran on epicycles and the centres of the epicycles on large circles. But the sun stood in the middle and earth was one of the planets. And Johannes Kepler, of the next generation of astronomers, finally removed the "ideal" circles and substituted the less ideal but correct ellipses. And while comparatively few people know that the sun is not in the centre of those ellipses but in one of the two focal points, most people do know that the planets move around the sun and that earth is one of the planets. Most of them

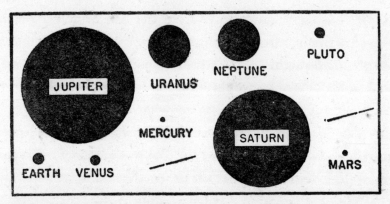

Fig. 6. The sizes of the planets of our solar system. Our moon and Jupiter's four large moons would appear slightly smaller than Mercury.

also know that all the planets move in the same direction in their orbits (counterclockwise, if you look at it from the North Pole of the sky) and that Mercury is the planet closest to the sun.

The sequence of the planets is one of the first things a student learns in "Elementary Astronomy." It reads: Mercury, Venus, Earth, Mars, Jupiter, Saturn, Uranus, Neptune, and Pluto. If Kepler could hear it he would be surprised by the last three names, because in his day and to his knowledge the solar system ended with ringed Saturn. But since his day the "Great Art of Astronomy," to use his own term, has advanced. In 1781 Herschel made the first addition to the list since classical times by discovering Uranus. Around the middle of the nineteenth century Neptune was discovered, and about a quarter-century ago Pluto became a name in the astronomical vocabulary.

While the planets are alike in a few respects (all move in elliptical orbits, all move in the same direction, all shine by reflected light) they differ from one another radically when it comes to details. There are planets with considerable atmospheres (in fact most of them have atmospheres) and there are planets without atmosphere. There are some which rotate rapidly on their axes and some that rotate more slowly. There are dense planets, like earth and Pluto, and there are others which are scarcely denser than water.

The inequality of their masses is especially noticeable. Of course the sun itself has much more mass than all the planets taken together (99⅞ per cent of the total of the solar system). But after the sun, Jupiter is the most massive

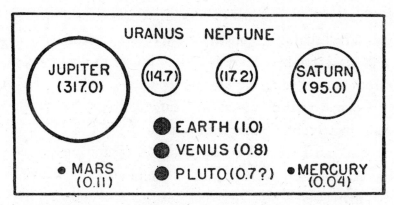

Fig. 7. The masses of the planets, represented by spheres of a uniform material (say iron) weighing as much as the planets actually do.

body, and Jupiter still has more mass than all the other planets together. And after Jupiter, the next in line, Saturn, is again more massive than all the remaining planets taken together.

If we look at the solar system as a whole the most astonishing fact is that it is so flat. If a precise scale model fitted into a round box 4 feet in diameter the box would have to be only 5 inches high. If you leave out Pluto and Mercury, the box can be reduced to a height of 3 inches.

Another remarkable fact is that the solar system is mostly empty space. You know that light travels with a velocity of 186,000 miles per second. At that speed it is only a little more than a second from the earth to the moon. When, some time in the future, somebody in the lunar observatory indulges in a telephone conversation with earth (say over a modulated light beam) there will be a pause of about 2½ seconds imposed by Nature between question and answer because of the time required by the carrier wave for the round trip.

But even at the rate with which light waves travel through space our own sun is 8 minutes distant, and to the nearest other sun it is 4.3 light years!

Nothing illustrates the comparative emptiness of the solar system better than the old method of a scale model—no matter how often it has been used, it is always impressive. Imagine the sun resting on a large building which you know well and from which you can judge distances. The sun is a glowing ball 50 feet in diameter. On that scale Mercury is within easy walking distance, some 2000 feet away. And it is a ball $2\frac{1}{4}$ inches in diameter. Venus is still within walking distance, about three-quarters of a mile from the model of the sun, and it is a larger ball—$5\frac{1}{2}$ inches in diameter. At 1 mile from the sun you find the earth, a ball slightly larger than that representing Venus, and 13 feet from the earth is a large ball-bearing ball $1\frac{1}{2}$ inches in diameter: our moon. At $1\frac{1}{4}$ miles from the sun you have Mars, 3 inches in diameter. At $2\frac{3}{4}$ miles you find a handful of scattered bird seed, the planetoids (*see* chapter 4), but at $5\frac{1}{4}$ miles there is a respectable sphere with a diameter of 5 feet: Jupiter. Within 20 feet of it you find four ball-bearing balls of over 2 inches diameter, its four large moons. Saturn is $9\frac{1}{2}$ miles from the sun in that model, and measures 4 feet 2 inches in diameter. One large ball-bearing ball and a number of small ones are scattered within 30 feet of it. So far, with a little straining, one could still talk of walking distances, but Uranus (a 22-inch ball) is 19 miles from the sun; Neptune (not quite an inch smaller than Uranus) is 30 miles away, and Pluto 41 miles on the average. But the ball representing Pluto is less than 5 inches in diameter. And even on that scale the nearest other sun would be 270,000 miles away, farther away than our moon actually is.

In spite of these distances and the relative emptiness of the solar system, space travel is possible. This is entirely due to those two outstanding features of the solar system mentioned earlier: the flatness of the system (in more precise language the planes of the orbits of the various planets show only very small inclinations), and the fact that the planets all move in the same direction.

To understand the importance of this latter fact we must realize that we have to change viewpoint when considering a trip from one planet to another —for example, a trip from earth to Mars or to Venus. In the case of the moon trip our viewpoint was the usual one: we used earth as a reference point. The trip to the moon took place essentially along one-half of a very narrow Keplerian ellipse with one of its focal points in the centre of the earth. But the ellipse which leads from earth to Mars has one of its focal points in the sun. Naturally many ellipses of this kind are possible, but they all have in common that one of their focal points coincides with the centre of the sun and that the ellipse itself either touches or crosses the orbits of both planets involved. From the standpoint of fuel consumption the ellipse which touches both orbits is the most economical.

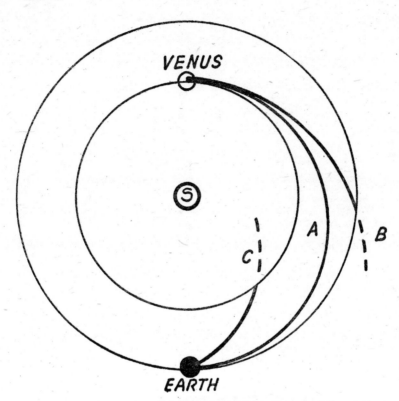

FIG. 8. Spaceship orbits. The drawing shows three possible orbits to Venus. The one labelled A, which *touches* both planetary orbits, is the most economical; the others, which *cross* one or the other orbit, are shorter and less time-consuming, but highly uneconomical in fuel consumption.   (From *Rockets and Space Travel*)

Since our own planet moves counterclockwise in its orbit, the ship will move counterclockwise too. It is easy to imagine what an impossible amount of braking action would have to be accomplished by the rocket motors if the target planet should move clockwise.

The earth moves in its orbit with a velocity of 18.5 miles per second and

93

the "front side" of this orbital motion is the "dawn side." Therefore a rocket ship taking off at dawn would add its own velocity to that of the earth. Since the velocity which the earth actually has is just enough to keep it in its orbit and to counteract the gravitational force of the sun, it follows that the ship taking off at dawn will be too fast for the sun to hold it in the orbit of earth. The ship will drift outward in the solar system and approach the orbit of Mars. The gravitational action of the sun, which is ever present, will slow down the ship so that when it reaches the orbit of Mars it will be going almost as slowly as Mars itself. (The orbital velocity of Mars is 15 miles per second.) Conversely, a ship taking off at sunset will subtract its own velocity from the orbital velocity of the earth. Seen from the sun, therefore, it will be too slow to stay in the earth's orbit and will drift inwards in the solar system, approaching the orbit of Venus. But in this case the action of the sun's gravity will increase the velocity of the ship so that its own speed, when it gets near the orbit of Venus, will not be too different from the orbital velocity of that planet, which is 21.7 miles per second.

If everything is timed right, the target planet will arrive at the "intersection point" at the same time as the ship, and a landing can be attempted.

All this is just a very rough outline of the fundamental concept of space-travel theory. The main fact to remember is that the ship has to add its own velocity to that of the earth if the target planet is farther away from the sun, and subtract its own velocity from that of the earth if the target planet is closer to the sun. As regards fuel requirements, it is interesting (and logical) to note that it is easier to go to Venus than to go to Mars, but also easier to return from Mars than from Venus.

It is also interesting to note that the fuel expenditure required for moving a spaceship from the orbit of earth to the orbit of either Mars or Venus is so small that it is well within the reach of contemporary rocket engineering. What keeps us from trying such space travel is the gravitational fields of the planets themselves. We could move a ship from the orbit of earth to the orbit of Venus, but we cannot lift it off our planet and also move it from orbit to orbit. Nor could we lift it off Venus. Even though the gravitational field of the sun is more powerful by far, it restrains us less than the fields of the planets do. The planetary fields have to be fought and overcome by the ship, while

94

the solar field can be utilized, and is actually helpful for one phase of each round trip.

It has been said about astronomy that it is both an exceptionally accurate and deplorably unreliable science, depending on what is in question. Ask an astronomer about the next eclipse that will be visible to a resident of Cape Town, South Africa, and he will provide the date to the fraction of a minute. Ask him what sort of calendar would be usable on Mars and he will come up not only with a workable design but with several choices. Ask any question that has to do with the movements of the heavenly bodies and a satisfactory answer will be forthcoming.

But the field where astronomical information shines forth with such an awe-inspiring aura of accuracy is really only "first-era knowledge," improved and incredibly refined by the optical instruments of the second era. If you ask questions which concern what we might call "second-era knowledge," the answers will be less definite, sometimes rather nebulous, and on occasion may consist only of the two words "not known." It almost seems that each era of astronomy does best when it comes to solving the problems of the preceding era. The inaccuracies of naked-eye observation were easily corrected by the optical instruments of the second era. The questions posed by the telescope—mostly concerning the surface conditions of the planets—will be answered by the spaceship. If that third era also poses new problems and questions without answering them, it will be up to the scientists of the third era to find ways and means towards a fourth era.

Of course we know well why the telescope poses so many questions without answering them. It is not so much that our optical instruments are not powerful enough. Nor is it entirely due to the fact that they operate from the bottom of, and hence through, an air ocean which often does not keep still and does not even always permit the use of the highest magnifications that exist. It is mostly because our observatories cannot change position in the solar system but have to stick to only one orbit in space.

When, on December 8, 1889, the Italian astronomer Giovanni Virginio Schiaparelli delivered a lecture to his King and Queen on the innermost planet of our system he began with the words: "Among the older planets no one is so difficult to observe as Mercury and none presents so many obstacles to investigation." Later on, during the same lecture, he emphasized this point once more by saying: "In the beginning of 1882 I determined to make a regular study of the planet; and in the eight following years I have had the telescope directed upon Mercury several hundreds of times, usually to little purpose, and with the loss of much time."

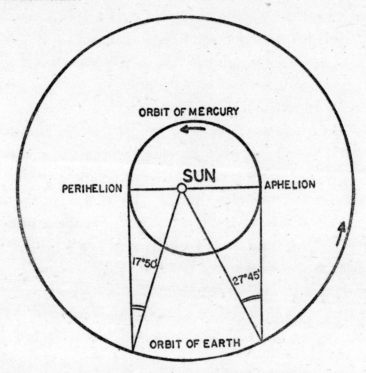

FIG. 9. The eccentricity of Mercury's orbit is so great that even the term "extreme elongation" does not always have the same meaning. It can vary from slightly less than 18 degrees to more than 27 degrees.

Most of the trouble experienced by Schiaparelli (and by everybody else who decided to devote his time and his skill to the "moon of the sun") is simply due to Mercury's nearness to our primary. Obviously a planet which is very near to the sun is hard to observe because it is always more or less strongly enveloped by the sun's brightness. To increase the difficulties, the planet is small—its diameter is only 3100 miles, or not quite 40 per cent of that of the earth. Adding insult to injury, the most elementary laws of Nature make it impossible even to see the planet when it is nearest to us. Mercury moves around the sun, inside the orbit of earth, in 88 of our days, and therefore presents its unilluminated "back" to us when nearest us, that is, when it is on the same side of the sun. Then a narrow sickle begins to show which gradually broadens. When the planet forms a right-angled triangle with the earth and the sun—astronomers call this an "extreme elongation," eastern or western as the case may be—we see just one-half of the disk illuminated. The fully illuminated disk is visible only when Mercury is at the opposite end of its orbit, but then it appears quite small and is hidden in the sun's brightness.

To the naked eye Mercury is visible only at dawn or dusk, and at first astronomers observed it only during those times. Because of some faint markings which seemed to be permanent and appeared very nearly in the same position every 24 hours, it was concluded that Mercury's rotation around its axis must be almost the same as that of earth. But Schiaparelli, by his diligent if tedious observations in daytime, proved differently: the planet had not rotated appreciably during those 24-hour intervals; its speed of rotation coincides with its speed of revolution, one complete turn in 88 days.

The result is that Mercury always points the same side towards the sun, just as does our moon with respect to the earth. Also, since the rate of rotation must be uniform but the rate of movement along the elliptical orbit cannot be uniform, there is libration. The permanently illuminated hemisphere is surrounded by a "twilight belt" where the sun rises and sets in the course of one of Mercury's year-days. Beyond the twilight belt there lies the hemisphere of eternal night, about three-sevenths of the total surface area of the planet.

Because of the libration the position of the sun in the sky of Mercury's illuminated hemisphere is not steady; it weaves back and forth through a fairly short arc. But because of the high eccentricity of Mercury's orbit something else takes place: to an observer on the sunlit side the sun appears to swell during the 44 days between aphelion and perihelion. After perihelion has been passed the sun recedes in size again until the description given in most books ("the sun appears three times as large as we see it") holds true.

That the nearness of the sun must cause a high surface temperature on Mercury has been clear ever since Schiaparelli established the length of its day. But the figures mentioned were mostly guesses: some said that "it might be hot enough to make water boil," and some others even ventured that it might be twice as hot as the boiling point of water. We don't have to guess any longer, since measurements made by Doctors Edison Pettit and Seth B. Nicholson of Mount Wilson and Palomar Observatories have provided us with the true figures. Using a vacuum thermocouple in connection with Mount Wilson's 100-inch reflector they found that the surface temperature at the centre of the sunlit hemisphere at perihelion is 770 degrees Fahrenheit. At that temperature both tin and lead are liquids and even zinc is quite close to melting (there is a difference of only 16 degrees Fahrenheit between the temperature mentioned and the melting point of zinc).

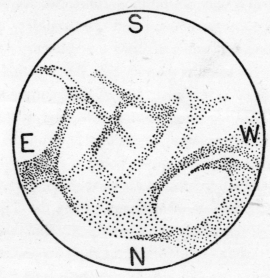

Fig. 10. Markings on Mercury, as drawn by Giovanni Schiaparelli.

The surface markings drawn by Schiaparelli (Fig. 10) are definitely permanent, but faint and hard to see. They look like mountain chains or like the outlines of what for want of a better term might be called continents. In fact the French astronomer E. M. Antoniadi, who pursued Mercury diligently for quite a long time with the aid of the 33-inch refractor of the observatory at Meudon, has filled in some of the spaces left white by Schiaparelli with a rather uniform grey. If we disregard the fact that one filled in spaces which the other left blank the two maps agree fairly well. Antoniadi, who worked 30 years after Schiaparelli had published his discoveries, also confirmed Schiaparelli's conclusion about the 88-day rotation of Mercury, which some had doubted during the intervening period. Schiaparelli and Antoniadi also agree that the markings seem to be obscured by "a faint whitishness" on occasion.

This statement has been greeted by some with enthusiasm as "proof" that Mercury has an atmosphere. Others, more cautious by inclination or experience or both, have pointed out that a failure to see faint markings is only negative evidence.

As these statements indicate, the problem of Mercury's atmosphere is not settled. Most of the evidence is against an atmosphere. To begin with, Mercury's albedo is the same as that of the moon—if the planet had any atmosphere worth mentioning, the albedo should be much higher. Both Mercury and our moon reflect some 7 per cent of the light they receive from the sun, while the earth was estimated to reflect 50 per cent. (More recent work indicates that this figure is somewhat high.)

Even a much thinner atmosphere than earth's, say one like that of Mars, should show up clearly on one special occasion: when Mercury performs a transit, crossing the disk of the sun as seen from earth. Almost all observers are agreed that they do not see indications of an atmosphere during transits. Furthermore, the sickle of the planet conforms to the geometrical shape one can calculate from its position. Venus, which has a very considerable atmosphere, shows "horns" which are much longer than they should be from such a calculation. Mercury does not. The counter-argument, however, is that the difference would be too small to be observable.

You remember that physicists could explain why there is no atmosphere on the moon: under the prevailing lunar midday temperatures the average velocity of the gas molecules would be close to the escape velocity of the moon. Unfortunately the conditions on Mercury are a sad borderline case as regards the escape of the atmosphere into space. Mercury's escape velocity is 2.3 miles per second, higher than that of the moon. But the temperatures are much higher, also, causing a much higher average velocity of the molecules. "Unfortunately," one is tempted to say, the temperatures are not high enough; no clear-cut case is presented. Even with the higher temperatures only the lightest gases would acquire average molecular velocities anywhere near 2.3 miles per second. That a noticeable percentage of oxygen and nitrogen molecules would escape is doubtful. Carbon-dioxide molecules certainly would not be able to escape.

They would not escape into space, that is. They might still escape in another manner. One-third of Mercury's surface never receives the faintest ray of sunlight. There we have an area of many thousands of square miles which must be cold, intensely cold. Presumably it is cold enough for gases to condense, to acquire not only the liquid but even the solid state. If there is a large area on a planet which is cold enough for gases to become solid, the whole atmosphere of the planet will collect in that area in time. The gases, being gases, will circulate into the area, but will not leave it again. Only two conditions are needed for this phenomenon to take place: that the area is cold enough, and that it is large enough. Also, of course, the process requires some time. But while we can be sure that there was time enough for this to happen, we cannot be sure that the dark side of Mercury is quite large enough, nor that it is quite cold enough.

In any event, it must have collected a large amount of the planet's original atmosphere, especially the heavier gases. And the lightest gases must have escaped into space. There cannot be much left. The whole argument can probably be settled with the compromise assumption that there is a residual atmosphere. Not enough to cause any of the definite phenomena which could be easily observed, but enough to account for those uncertain indications which caused the argument in the first place.

Venus, the brightly shining morning and evening star, Hesperus and Phosphorus of the ancients, moves around the sun between Mercury and earth. It therefore approaches earth much more closely than Mercury—in fact it comes closer than any other planet. But while Mercury presents difficulties,

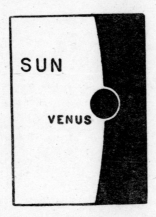

Fig. 11. "Transit" of Venus. When the planet Venus crosses the disk of the sun, a rather rare event, its atmosphere is made conspicuously visible by refraction. No such phenomenon occurs during a transit of Mercury.

Venus presents mysteries. We know less about Venus than we do about Mercury.

Oh, we *are* sure about a number of things. Venus is almost a second earth as far as size goes. Its diameter is only 200 miles less than that of earth. The mass is 80 per cent of that of our rather massive home planet. The albedo is 59 per cent, the highest albedo in the solar system. Venus most decidedly has an atmosphere. The Venus year is 224.7 of our days long, a fact easily explained by the tighter orbit and higher orbital velocity. Venus's orbit is the most nearly circular one in the whole solar system and the disk of Venus the most nearly perfect circle—it does not show any traces of an equatorial bulge.

That short paragraph contains the sum total of the definite knowledge we have about the planet which approaches us more closely than any other. The causes of our knowing so little are the facts that were cited in the case of Mercury, plus the dense atmosphere of Venus. Venus is also inside earth's orbit and appears dark when closest. And what we see seems always to be just atmosphere and mostly the upper layers of that atmosphere. Only on rare occasions have astronomers succeeded in looking into it. In February 1913 a very definite indentation was observed in the terminator, the line bounding the illuminated part of the planet. It was seen by a number of observers in different localities, but whether it actually was a 40-mile-high mountain, as some enthusiastic writers wanted to make out, is more than doubtful. It might have been a local, if large, disturbance of the atmosphere caused by a gigantic volcanic explosion. The most famous terrestrial example of that kind is the explosion of the volcano Rakata on the island of Krakatoa on August 27, 1883, which blew the whole island apart, threw a cubic mile of dust and pumice at least 8 miles into the air, caused dust clouds in the upper stratosphere which persisted for years, and was noisy enough to be heard on the island of Rodriguez, 2968 miles away.

A dark marking photographed at Mount Wilson on June 26, 1927, might also have been caused by a volcanic explosion. It is easier to imagine that a catastrophe of such a type lifted dark ground material to layers of the Venusian atmosphere where it became visible to us than to imagine natural forces suddenly creating a hole in the atmosphere through which we could look down to the ground. Occasionally markings are not darker but brighter than the generally bright "surface" of the planet.

Both Giovanni Schiaparelli of Milan and Percival Lowell of Flagstaff devoted much time to the observation of Venus. It may be mentioned in passing that much of this work was carried on in the daytime, because Venus, whenever it is in the sky at all, can be seen in the daytime, even with the naked eye, provided you know where to look for it. Napoleon is reported to have seen Venus accidentally by looking in the right direction when he started his march into Russia. He took it to be a good omen.

By watching what markings they could, both Schiaparelli and Lowell came to the conclusion that the older idea of a 24-hour day on Venus was wrong. Both decided that Venus had a year-day like Mercury, with a permanently sunlit and a permanently cold hemisphere, separated by a twilight belt reaching around the planet and at most 1000 miles wide.

While we still don't know the length of a Venusian day, we can be sure that the conclusion about the year-day, advocated by Schiaparelli first and supported by Lowell later, is wrong. The dark side of Venus would be cold enough and certainly would be large enough to have collected practically all of the available water and a very large amount of the atmosphere. If we assume that the virtually unbroken whiteness we see is essentially water vapour, layer upon unbroken cloud layer, we also have to assume that Venus has a day different in length from the length of its year. It does not have to be a 24-hour day, it may be 48 hours, 80 hours, or even 100 hours. But there would have to be at least 60 or 80 Venus days per Venus year.

At this point the narrative has to be interrupted for a moment to look at the instruments at the disposal of our second-era astronomers. There are four of these instruments (each one, of course, existing in a large number of types and designs) and they are all variations on the principle of the human eye. But they are strange and wonderful variations. The simplest is the one that came first, the telescope itself. It is a larger eye, with more light-gathering power and more resolving power (usually referred to as magnification), and has the effect "to make distant objects appear close" as Galileo Galilei wrote when the instrument was new.

The second is the camera, which not only produces a permanent record but has another fine feature in addition. A faint object does not become any clearer or more definite to your eye if you stare at it for a long time—indeed, because of eyestrain and fatigue, the contrary is true. But the photographic plate operates the other way round: faint impressions strengthen with time, and the camera can produce a fine sharp picture of a faint and distant galaxy, for example, which could never have been seen directly with such clearness of fine detail.

The third instrument is the thermocouple, a quite different kind of "eye." To make the explanation short: it "sees" heat rays—you remember that astronomers measured the temperature of the lunar surface and of the surface of Mercury at perihelion.

The fourth is the spectroscope, which can ascertain the chemical composition of distant bodies. It is based on the principle, discovered accidentally about a century ago, that each chemical element, when heated, sends out a light of a specific wave length, or collection of wave lengths. What is called a "spectrum" is a beam of light, say sunlight, that has been spread out into a long narrow band by means of a set of prisms. In the case of sunlight this band shows the rainbow colours from red to violet. But within this long band vertical lines appear and the position of these lines indicates the chemical elements which send out the light.

It isn't difficult in principle. The hard work is the proper application of the principle. At first most of the hard work consisted of finding out by experiment which element produced what lines and where; and what the gases of the atmosphere through which light passed did to lines the light originally contained, and so forth. Now the hard work consists mostly in untangling lines. Only a very few elements produce just a few lines; most of them cause whole sets. And one of the lines of element A is only too likely to obscure a line of element B, which, in turn and in wonderful collaboration with element A, may blot out the lines of elements C and D.

In addition to showing the lines of the elements, the spectroscope does something else. If you have a nice strong line of one element but it is not quite where it should be, you know that the light source is moving. If that line has slipped in the direction of the red end of the spectrum it means that the light source is moving away from the observer. If the line has slipped in the direction of the blue-violet end it means that the light source is approaching. Naturally the amount of "slippage" is an indicator of the speed of movement.

It need hardly be mentioned that astronomers have pointed not only their telescopes at Venus, "usually to little purpose and with the loss of much time." They have also used their cameras—and if they fail to complain about lack of good results it is only because astronomers are hardened to disappointments. They have used thermocouples which showed that substantial amounts of heat were radiated by the centre of the *dark* side—proving at least that the dark side cannot be permanently dark. And they have used their spectroscopes also, both to try to find out something about the composition of the atmosphere and to detect rotation. When a planet rotates, obviously one side—called "limb" in astronomical parlance—approaches the observer and the other recedes. The chemical part of the search had one positive result: the presence of gaseous carbon dioxide on Venus was definitely established.

As regards rotation, the indications were absolutely negative. This, however, could still mean a rather slow rotation. Anything slower than, say, one turn in 72 hours would not be detectable by the spectroscope. But then William H. Pickering came up with an ingenious thought. The axis of rotation of our own planet does not stand vertically on the plane of the orbit. It deviates from the vertical by about $23\frac{1}{2}$ degrees, thus causing our seasons. But the axis of Jupiter does stand almost upright on the plane of its orbit. So does that of Mercury. These planets resemble spinning gyroscopes. Uranus, on the other hand, lies virtually flat, the direction of its axis roughly the same as the plane of its orbit. It can be compared to a rolling ball instead of an upright gyroscope.

Pickering, after spending much time observing Venus, announced that the period of rotation was 68 hours, but that Venus, like Uranus, had its axis in the plane of the orbit. This would explain why the spectroscopic investigation was such a failure: there had been no approaching and receding limbs because at that time the axis of Venus had pointed at earth. Pickering's idea has been accepted by a small number of astronomers, but majority opinion seems to be in favour of a more conventional position of the axis and a slow rotation.

With so little knowledge about the planet any guess at surface conditions

104

can be only a guess. The spectroscope has revealed that there is carbon dioxide in the atmosphere in comparatively large amounts—probably around 3 per cent, which is a hundred times as much as earth has. Since carbon dioxide is highly efficient in absorbing and retaining heat a powerful "greenhouse effect" must result, especially since Venus is closer to the sun than we are. The air over its ground must be hot. That much had been guessed earlier and the heat accounted beautifully for the eternal cloud layers. Pictures of a most luxuriant jungle with voracious monsters in a permanent warm fog were painted with pen and brush.

But the spectroscope could not find oxygen, which the plants would produce, nor could it find water. Consequently, we have to assume either that because of very special—and by no means readily explicable—conditions no water vapour ever gets high enough to make the spectroscope respond, or else that, strange as it may seem, there is no abundant water on Venus. Dr. Frank E. Ross of Mount Wilson Observatory was the first to utter this sacrilegious thought, and so far no fact has been found which contradicts his idea of the surface conditions on Venus. According to his hypothesis the surface consists of dry reddish soil, heated to about the boiling point of water. There must be a considerable temperature difference between the day and night sides, resulting in permanent strong winds, a perpetual sandstorm which has eroded most of the rock formations. What we see in the telescope is merely an upper cirrus veil, occasionally torn by an especially violent storm.

Nobody can tell whether this is actually the true picture. It does conform to what knowledge we have. But our knowledge is very small indeed.

Our nearest neighbour beyond the earth in relation to the sun is Mars.

More has been written about Mars than about any other planet, more than about all the other planets together. The volume of literature on a subject does not always indicate the volume of knowledge about it. Primarily it is an indication of the amount of thought spent on it and the amount of interest. But that implies again that there is something to think about and something to be interested in.

Actually, however, we do know more about Mars than about any other heavenly body except the sun and the moon. We begin with some figures.

Mars is a smaller world, with a diameter of about 4200 miles as compared to the 7900-mile diameter of earth. There are a few minor difficulties in measuring it—visual and photographic diameters do not agree completely and a photograph taken through an orange filter does not agree completely with a photograph taken through a violet filter. The difference is obviously caused by the Martian atmosphere and the question hinges mostly on the depth you assign to the atmosphere. But 4200 miles must be quite close to the actual diameter and 60 miles is the figure most generally accepted for the depth of

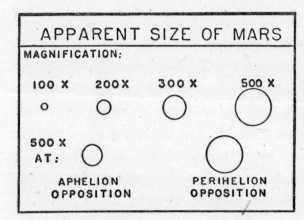

Fig. 12. Apparent size of Mars. The two circles in the bottom row explain why astronomers always wait for perihelion oppositions. Top row shows apparent sizes for different magnifications at perihelion opposition. To realize how Mars appears even at perihelion opposition and with a magnification of 500 diameters, draw a circle measuring 11/16 inch in diameter and look at it from a distance of 1 foot.

the atmosphere. The Martian atmosphere is thin and transparent and shows only occasional cloud formations.

Mars turns around an axis which is tilted just a shade more than that of earth, 25 degrees 10 minutes as compared to our 23 degrees 27 minutes. The length of the Martian day is also a trifle more than ours: it is 24 hours, 37 minutes, and 22.58 seconds. After all the trouble with the Venusian day it is an exceptional pleasure to have such a precise figure. One revolution of Mars around the sun takes 687 of our days or, since the Martian day is slightly longer, 668 Martian days. Its surface gravity is 0.38 that of earth, which means that a 100-pound bag of potatoes would weigh only 38 pounds on Mars, but, if brought there, it would still have the nutritional value of a hundred terrestrial pounds. The escape velocity works out to 3.1 miles per second, as compared to our 7 miles per second. The orbital velocity is naturally less than that of earth, since Mars is farther away from the sun. It is 15 miles per second, $3\frac{1}{2}$ miles per second slower than earth's. The mean distance of Mars from the sun is 141,650,000 miles. And its orbit is much more highly elliptical than that of earth—Kepler made his discovery of the ellipticity of planetary orbits by investigating the orbit of Mars. If Mars' orbit were as nearly circular as ours, the fact that it is an ellipse might not have been found then, because Tycho Brahe's naked-eye observations would not have been precise enough to make the difference obvious.

Since Mars moves around the sun outside of our own orbit we see it always in full illumination. The maximum of the dark hemisphere which can

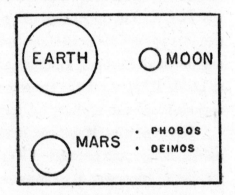

FIG. 13. Earth, moon, and Mars, drawn to scale. As a rule of thumb one may remember that Mars has about twice the diameter of our moon and earth about twice the diameter of Mars. (The two dots for Phobos and Deimos are a bit too large!)

appear to us hardly slices one-eighth off the disk. Since Mars needs not quite 2 years to get round the sun once, earth and Mars find themselves together in the same direction from the sun approximately every 2 years and 2 months. This figure changes a little from case to case because neither of the two orbits is circular: the shortest possible interval between two such oppositions, as they are called, is 2 years and 36 days and the longest 2 years and 78 days. But one opposition is not as good as another. Even though our own orbit is very nearly circular we are still farther away from the sun at one time during the year than at other times. Our own aphelion is in midsummer, unless you happen to be an Australian, for whom it is in midwinter. It is interesting to note that the seasonal changes on the northern hemisphere are the precise opposite of what the distance from the sun would indicate. In the case of earth the tilt of the axis is far more important than the comparatively slight difference between perihelion and aphelion.

Fortunately the perihelion of the Martian orbit, as regards direction as seen from the sun, lies close to earth's aphelion. This means that an opposition of Mars and earth occurring in midsummer (northern hemisphere seasons) is a much closer opposition than one occurring in midwinter. One occurring late in August is the most useful, one occurring in February is least so. The differences are quite large, the actual distance between the two planets being 35 million miles in an August opposition, and 63 million miles in a February opposition.

The opposition of 1948 was a poor specimen, the one due in 1950 will hardly be better, and those due in 1963 and 1965 will be equally bad. They are all January, February, and March oppositions. The July opposition of 1939 was fine, the fall opposition of 1941 was all right, the late August opposition due in 1956 will be perfection (unless we have bad weather all over America and northern Europe), and the early August opposition in 1971 will be almost as good. What we don't know now we may learn then, even if we are not optimistic enough to expect a telescope on the moon by 1971.

For centuries Mars was interesting on two counts only: because of its reddish colour and because of Kepler's work on its orbit. Galilei reported that the disk of Mars was of uniform colour without markings. Later astronomers, somewhat aghast on hearing this, have used telescopes of the type and power of those used by Galilei and have found that he reported correctly—as far as the power of his instruments went. Mars is no easy object, even during a good opposition, because of its small size. Granted a good opposition, perfect seeing conditions, and a really powerful instrument, you still get only something that looks like a small marble on the palm of your outstretched hand. Some time after Galilei, an astronomer by the name of Fontana made the first sketch of Mars. This sketch shows a dark round spot in the centre, surrounded by a grey ring, obviously mostly the result of eyestrain, although the centre spot may have been a blurred image of the most conspicuous marking, now called *Syrtis major*.

Mars leaped into prominence in 1877 because of a good opposition. During that opposition Asaph Hall discovered that Mars had two tiny moons, just as had been "prophesied" in *Gulliver's Travels*, an amazing case of the purest coincidence known to the history of science. And during that same opposition Giovanni Schiaparelli saw, for the first time, the "canals of Mars." As has been explained many times by many writers, the Italian word *canali*, as used by

Schiaparelli, really means "channel" and the meaning "canal" is secondary. But even people who knew Italian disregarded such niceties. The thought of having found another inhabited planet brushed all caution aside. From then on it was Mars, Mars, Mars—it was continents and canals, seas and islands.

Schiaparelli, who personally was quite cautious about the *canali*, was convinced that the dark areas on Mars were actually seas while the light areas were continents, mostly desert. And in most books you can read that on earth the seas cover three-quarters of the surface of the globe, while on Mars the land covers three-quarters of the surface. With water so rare what was more logical than that the Martians should have covered their continents with a network of canals meeting in "lakes" (which, however, were taken to be artificial bodies of water), in order to irrigate their deserts?

Drawings were made (and, of course, published) showing the engineering features which those canals had to have. The high whitish clouds which appeared near the rim of Mars and shone brightly, illuminated by the sun, were interpreted as signals of the Martians. Realizing that at least the nights of Mars must be very cold, it was conjectured that the Martian cities were underground, and presumably the canals served for irrigation only and not for transportation as had been thought at first. Of course one could not be sure whether the canals might not be lined by highways on both sides—after all, what we did see could not be the canals alone, because a line on the surface of Mars, even if contrasting sharply with the surrounding desert, would have to be at least 50 miles wide to be visible from earth. What we did see were obviously the lines of vegetation in the desert, produced with the aid of the irrigation canals. And there was no way of telling what this vegetation might hide; earthly cities happen to be generally circular in shape because they have spread in all directions from an original centre. Martian cities might spread lengthwise along the canals. Even if they did not, a 50-mile-wide strip of vegetation could hide a very large city.

Then the pendulum swung back. It was all a mistake. The canals were optical illusions, caused by eyestrain and by the effort to see details below the limits of visibility. Those colour changes, and especially those reported by Percival Lowell from his Flagstaff Observatory built especially for the purpose of establishing the Martians (this statement was an exaggeration in itself) were mere wishful thinking. The dark areas were not seas but something like the Asiatic salt steppes, only much saltier, too salty for anything to grow. And even the white polar caps which were to have furnished the irrigation water were not water at all but frozen carbon dioxide—not ice, but dry ice.

Suppose all these dismal statements were correct (which they are not), Mars would have remained a highly interesting planet about which we knew much more than we did about featureless Venus or sun-scorched Mercury. But after all the imaginative tracing of Martian superengineering, the disappointment, especially to the layman, was enormous.

The present concepts of Mars are different again. In looking at them one should, as far as possible, forget what went before. Excluding earth, Mars is still the planet about which we know most and the most interesting planet in the solar system, and it is still the one that is most similar to earth.

One might say that most of Mars was never touched by the violent clash of opinions and interpretations: the light areas which cover three-fourths of the planet were deserts to Schiaparelli and Lowell, they were deserts to their opponents, and they are still deserts to modern astronomers. In colour they range from some definitely yellow areas to reddish and dark brick-red areas. The conclusion is inevitable that much of the oxygen that must have been in the Martian atmosphere is tied up in those deserts. The darker areas are certainly not seas. If they were seas one should see the bright reflection of the sun in them. Generations of astronomers, literally speaking, have watched for such light flashes without success. There is some uncertain evidence that the light areas are higher than the dark areas. The difference in elevation is not large, measured by earthly standards, presumably 1000 or 2000 feet. Incidentally there are no real mountains anywhere on Mars.

The polar caps are water, or rather ice. That carbon-dioxide theory slipped badly by disregarding the fact that not only do the white polar caps disappear as the Martian spring changes into Martian summer, but a darker area forms around them in the process. In other words one can see them melt. But carbon dioxide does not assume the liquid state at all under what we call "normal" atmospheric pressure. It goes directly from the gaseous to the solid state and vice versa—hence "dry" ice. It is true that the polar caps of Mars should not be compared to those of earth. They are not masses of ice and snow

110

several miles in thickness. Since we know pretty well how hot the sunshine can be on Mars and since our ideas about the atmospheric pressure there cannot be too far from the truth, it is possible to calculate how deep the snow can be and still melt completely in summer. The Martian polar caps must have an average thickness considerably less than a foot or they would not melt completely. A Martian polar cap probably corresponds to a snowfall of a few inches. The total probably would not quite fill one of the Great Lakes.

But there is water on Mars.

There are also clouds. The more frequent type is yellow clouds which are obviously sandstorms—or dust storms. Another type is called "blue" clouds with reference to the fact that they show bright in blue and violet light but are invisible in the infra-red. Those "blue" clouds do not persist long and are most frequent in the polar regions. They are probably thin mists of ice crystals.

The air is thin, far too thin for the use of man or of the kind of animal life we know on earth. The spectroscope has failed to discover either water vapour or oxygen with certainty, but there is an explanation for that. The eye can see water, either liquid or frozen, the spectroscope can detect *vapour* only. As for oxygen, the lines which the Martian atmosphere would cause are greatly "strengthened" by the lines which originate from oxygen in our own atmosphere. They are "strengthened" so much that they are simply blotted out by our lines. The problem is to decide whether the lines appear stronger than our own atmosphere would make them. The difference is too small to permit a definite conclusion. That particular problem will have to wait until we can take a spectrogram outside of our own atmosphere, and it might be settled that way even before that fine opposition of 1956.

But while the spectroscope is not much good when used on the thin atmosphere of Mars, the vacuum thermocouple has produced a few heat measurements. At noon the temperature at the Martian equator was found to be around 50 degrees Fahrenheit generally and around 72 degrees Fahrenheit in the dark areas. Positions near the rim of the disk give indications that the temperature at sunrise and sunset is about 10 degrees Fahrenheit. The night must be cold in an emphatic manner but we don't see enough of Mars' dark side to make a measurement.

The main feature of the Martian landscape must be stark monotony. No mountains, no real cloud formations, no bodies of open water, not much weather except for the daily temperature changes. Not even the two moons provide much change. The farther moon, Deimos, which is also the smaller, would appear just as a bright star to the unaided eye. It would need 59.6 hours from rising to setting and would run through its phases twice in succession during that time, but a small telescope would be needed to observe the phases. Phobos, the nearer and somewhat larger moon, would rise every 11 hours and be in the sky for 4 hours and 20 minutes at a time. It is so close that an observer could not see a full half of its revolution because of the bulk of the planet. For the same reason—the combination of nearness and the non-transparency of the planet itself—the moons would not be visible at all to explorers in the polar regions.

Still, we are justified in believing in life on Mars—hardy plant life. The colour changes which we can see are explained most logically and most simply by assuming vegetation. From a terrestrial landscape—Tibet—we can get a good idea of what to expect. Dr. Robert S. Richardson of Mount Wilson and Palomar Observatories found a description of Tibet which might be written specifically for the purpose of depicting probable conditions on Mars.

> . . . The life in Tibet is in many particulars the life of a desert waste. It differs from the deserts of Arabia or Sahara in one particular: it has none of their intensive heat. But otherwise Tibet is essentially a desert, empty, bleak and bare.
>
> As we travel across it we see all the features of the desert, the wide tracts of brown and barren soil, the vast distances spread out before the eye, the fierce display of light. Here, as in the desert, we meet tracts of sand, often loose and crumbling and at the mercy of the wind. . . .
>
> There is a great range of temperature characteristic of the desert, often fifty degrees between day and night. The atmosphere is so dry that it splits the skin and nails, and prevents the ordinary decomposition of flesh. Fierce winds blow across it. . . . We observe the same scantiness of vegetation, the monotonous growth that gives no colour to the landscape, the absence of trees, the thorniness of the plants, the short active season in which flowers bloom rapidly and as rapidly die away. . . .[1]

Of terrestrial plants, lichen might survive transplanting to Mars and one may imagine that some of the desert flora of Tibet could be adapted. At any

[1] From "Animal Life at High Altitudes" by Major R. W. G. Hingston (*Geographical Journal*, March 1925), quoted by Dr. Robert S. Richardson in an article entitled "New Paths to New Planets," *Air Trails and Science Frontiers*, September 1947.

event conditions are such that life as we know it would find the going tough, but not impossible.

And now the "canals." Even aside from the matter of interpretation, astronomers were divided into two groups. One group simply stated that they saw the canals and drew what they saw. The other stated equally simply that they could not see any canals, no matter how hard they tried. Under these circumstances one could only wait and hope that the question might be decided later in some manner. And a recent report by Dr. Edison Pettit of Mount Wilson and Palomar Observatories tends to explain part of that mystery. Doctor Pettit had observed Mars during the oppositions of 1907 and 1909 and had also done some work during those of 1924 and 1926. He had not seen any canals on any of these occasions and therefore had no reason to believe in their existence.

In the summer of 1939, when Mars was close, he began some observations of the planet in his backyard observatory in Pasadena, with a telescope containing an excellent six-inch lens made by Alvan Clarke & Sons. His programme was begun largely as a matter of self-education, to see if he could verify the well-known change in tint of the markings with progress of the Martian seasons. He had no thought of seeing the canals, which he naturally supposed were far beyond the range of so small an instrument.

Early on the morning of July 6, 1939, he was working at the six-inch, trying to discern the character of a large oval marking on the disk. He had made an outline sketch under fair seeing conditions, but by the time it was finished the seeing had improved so much that he felt dissatisfied with it. Then while concentrating upon the boundary between a dark and light area it happened—a canal flashed out, followed almost immediately by another one! In the next few hours two more canals were seen, sometimes the four being visible simultaneously. Towards morning a southern California fog came in, abruptly putting a stop to observations of Mars and its canal system.

On the following nights, although the definition was not as good as formerly, he was able to see the canals originally observed, in addition to several others. He decided not to consult the maps of Mars so that the drawings would be more valuable as constituting independent observations free from bias. During 1939 he completed a map of the planet using both the six-inch and a twenty-inch reflector on Mt. Wilson. A total of forty canals was recorded.[1]

[1] Richardson, op. cit.

It might be added at this point that the photographing of Martian canals is such an exceedingly difficult job that some astronomers do not accept as evidence photographs showing one or several of the most prominent canals. It may be caution carried too far, but naturally astronomers want only the most definite and incontrovertible kind of evidence when it comes to a question like the Martian canals. But it is hard to contradict an experience like that of Dr. Pettit.

As of 1949: the canals of Mars do exist.

What they are will not be decided until astronomy has entered into its next era.

Beyond Mars there is the realm of the dwarfs, the asteroids or planetoids, which receive more attention in chapter 4. Over fifteen hundred of them are known and registered at present. Twenty times that number probably exist unknown and unrecorded; like the number of lunar craters, the number of bodies in the planetoid belt depends on the resolving power of the instrument used and on the amount of work expended.

And beyond the realm of the dwarfs, just as the fairy tales always insisted, there is the kingdom of the giants. Only the giants are not numerous. There are only four of them: Jupiter the Big, Saturn the Beautiful, Uranus the Freak, and Neptune the Lonely One. As regards size, Uranus and Neptune are close rivals, while Saturn stands intermediate between them and Jupiter.

The four giants show many and fundamental similarities, and are so different from the inner planets that one can hardly believe that they are planets of the same sun. All four are enormous as compared to the inner planets and while they are of necessity slow in their orbits they rotate very fast around their axes. Jupiter's enormous bulk rotates in 9 hours and 55 minutes, Saturn's in 10 hours and 14 minutes, Uranus's in 10 hours and 40 minutes, and Neptune's in 15 hours and 40 minutes. They all have enormously deep atmospheres. In fact, we do not know just how deep down "solid ground" begins, and the diameters in the table (page 14) refer to the planets plus their atmospheres. That we have to measure the diameters of the atmospheres also accounts to some extent for the very low average densities which we have to assign to these planets. Those of Jupiter, Uranus, and Neptune work out as only slightly higher than the density of water, while that of Saturn is even less than that of water.

Except for Neptune they all have numerous moons. Neptune probably has more than the one we know but the planet is so far away that its presumed smaller moons have not to date been detected. And while highly developed spaceships of the future will probably pay at least one visit to each of these many moons it is certain that the planets will never be visited. Jupiter's surface conditions, especially, must be such that no human being, no matter how well prepared and protected with special equipment, could survive for any reasonable length of time.

If this statement had been made in 1900 all professional astronomers would have agreed, just as they will today. But the reasons for agreeing with that statement have changed greatly.

To the naked eye Jupiter is very often the brightest star in the sky and is, for that reason, often confused with Venus by a casual observer. The simplest way to make sure is to look late in the evening, since Venus sets early and Jupiter does not. Even with the weakest optical assistance, Jupiter presents a disk to the view, and a slightly better telescope shows not only the cloud markings that run across the disk like the degrees of latitude across a globe but also the flattening of Jupiter's sphere. The flattening—the ratio of equatorial to polar diameter is about 15:14—is caused by the rapidity of rotation, which is such that a point at Jupiter's equator moves with a speed within a few hundred feet per second of the escape velocity for the earth! While the light from Jupiter is yellow to the naked eye, the telescopic view shows a great deal of reddish tint. From its size, low density, and colour, astronomers drew the only too natural conclusion that Jupiter was still hot, molten, and glowing to a slight extent with its own light. The case seemed decided when, first in 1878, a phenomenon appeared which was named the "Great Red Spot."

This was an elliptical area not far from Jupiter's equator, some 30,000 miles in length and half that wide. At first it was thought that one of the Minor Planets had crashed on Jupiter, causing a lava flow covering a half-million square miles. Then for a while the Red Spot deepened in colour, as if it were rising to higher layers, and simultaneously it was found to lag behind the rotation of Jupiter. Astronomers congratulated themselves on actually witnessing the formation of a new moon. Nothing happened, however. The Red Spot has slowly faded ever since, although it is still easily visible. It has also strayed from its original position by about one-quarter of the circumference of the planet.

Early spectroscopic work added another intriguing touch. There was a line in the spectrogram which did not seem to correspond with anything except a strong line given off by chlorophyll, the green substance in plants which somehow builds starches from water, carbon dioxide, and sunlight. This line was found in all four outer planets, being strongest, it seemed, on Neptune. The conclusion was that since life could not yet exist on the hot surfaces of these planets it therefore floated about in the atmosphere as "aerial plankton," comparable to the plankton of our oceans!

All these ideas held until about 1920; then they began to crumble. Suppose Jupiter did not produce any heat of its own, what would its temperature be? Calculation, reluctantly accepted, showed that it must be around minus 200 degrees Fahrenheit. Later thermocouple measurements gave readings corresponding to minus 210 degrees Fahrenheit. That wonderful chlorophyll line was resolved into what is known as "absorption bands" of ammonia and methane. And in 1932 Rupert Wildt of Princeton came up with a new concept of the structure of the outer planets which has been generally accepted since (Fig. 14).

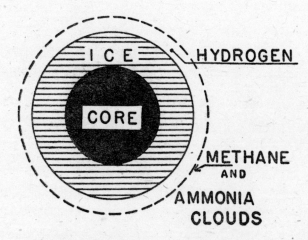

FIG. 14. Cross section through the planet Jupiter. The core is assumed to be metallic and rocky, overlaid by thousands upon thousands of miles of ice, with a hydrogen atmosphere and ammonia clouds.

He assumed that they all started with an abundance of hydrogen atoms which would not escape because of the large masses and high gravitational forces involved. First the metallic elements would form a core, then the hydrogen would combine with oxygen to form water (H_2O), with nitrogen to form ammonia (NH_3), and with carbon to form methane (CH_4), all compounds which use large amounts of hydrogen. The ice would form a thick sheath around the metallic core, going through various little-known stages because of the enormous pressures on the inner layers. The remaining hydrogen would form a deep atmosphere with clouds of methane and of ammonia crystals. This outer cloud layer is all that we actually observe with telescope, camera, thermocouple, and spectroscope.

Whether Jupiter has actually "quieted down" completely is doubtful. Its atmosphere and its "surface" may still undergo violent changes—after all, the Red Spot does exist and so does the so-called "South Tropical Disturbance." These disturbances may be called "volcanic," although they are more likely to be chemical explosions of hydrogen, caused possibly by sodium, or other chemical reactions which are not in our low-pressure chemistry. All this amid cliffs of permanent ice rising from a sea of temporarily liquid ammonia!

Compared to this picture, the surfaces of Jupiter's moons must be almost familiar. Four of the moons, discovered by Galileo Galilei, are enormous in size. No. III (Ganymede) and No. IV (Callisto) are larger than Mercury. No. I (Io) is larger than our moon while No. II (Europa) is only slightly smaller than our moon. The other seven are tiny bodies. Some of them, like No. III and possibly No. IV, point the same face to Jupiter all the time, but since they move around Jupiter within a few of our days the entire surface of each is exposed to the sun at regular short intervals. However, they are too far away from the sun for that to be useful. There will be light but no heat. Europa, the smallest of the "big four," has an exceptionally high albedo, probably caused by a frozen atmosphere. Of the smaller moons, No. v is of interest because of its nearness to the planet, and No. VIII, No. IX, and No. XI violate all rules by being "retrograde," which means that they move in the opposite direction from the usual direction in the solar system. The moons were numbered in the order of discovery. Counting from the planet out their sequence is: V, I, II, III, IV, VI, VII, X, XI, VIII, IX.

Saturn is the showpiece of the solar system. On visitor's night in the observatory, the public asks first for the canals of Mars and then for the "planet with rings." And while Mars is inevitably disappointing to laymen, Saturn usually surpasses their expectations. Although the rings look quite substantial (and are somewhat brighter than the planet itself), they are remarkably thin. If one wanted to cut a scale model of the rings out of paper, and make the proportion between width and thickness correct, one would have to make the outer diameter about 60 inches if the paper is ordinary newsprint! That anything of such proportions could not be solid was clear fairly early in modern astronomy. The rings had to consist of numberless separate particles. More recent observation has confirmed this view. In accordance with Kepler's laws, the inner parts of the rings revolve around the planet faster than the outer portions. And the disturbances causes by the gravitational attraction of the largest moon is responsible for the gap which has been named "Cassini's division." The particles composing the rings must be mostly small, the lower size limit about that of grains of beach sand. Still finer particles would drift from their orbits because of the pressure exerted by sunlight on very small bodies. The total mass of the rings is about 1/100 of that of our moon.

Of Saturn's nine moons, three are of special interest: No. vi (Titan, the largest), No. viii (Japetus), and No. ix (Phoebe). Of course No. x (Themis) is interesting too by reason of having been lost, unless Professor Pickering was simply mistaken when he announced its discovery in 1905. Phoebe, the smallest of Saturn's moons, is retrograde like Jupiter's smallest moons. Japetus, about half the size of our moon, has one side which is five times brighter than the other. No explanation is known, but there can be no doubt about the fact itself. And finally Titan, considerably larger than our moon, is the only satellite in the whole system that has an atmosphere. Professor G. P. Kuiper succeeded in obtaining a spectrogram of that atmosphere and found it to contain large amounts of methane. The presence of ammonia is suspected too. Titan's atmosphere, therefore, is of the same type as the atmospheres of the outer planets.

Beyond Saturn the solar system gets bleak. Uranus freakishly rolls along its orbit with its axis tilted at 98 degrees, a little more than a right angle. Its four larger moons and the recently discovered tiny fifth moon revolve in the plane of the planet's equator so that their orbits are almost vertical to the orbit of the planet and are technically retrograde. In structure Uranus must be like Jupiter and Saturn, but there is more methane and less ammonia in its atmosphere. The "surface" temperature is minus 300 degrees Fahrenheit.

When Herschel discovered Uranus in 1781, he thought at first that he had discovered a comet. Then the planetary nature of the new body was established and later it occurred to astronomers that it had actually betrayed its existence by disturbing Saturn's orbit slightly. Naturally they kept a sharp watch on the motion of Uranus to see whether new irregularities might betray still another planet. When they seemed to, John C. Adams in England and Urbain J. J. Leverrier in Paris went to work. Both succeeded, but Leverrier published his work as he went along and Adams did not. Adams also had the bad luck that the English observer who was entrusted with the search was quite sloppy and careless. He missed the planet. Leverrier sent his calculations to Berlin, where Galle found the new planet on September 23, 1846. Leverrier disbelieved the actually well-founded British claims and at first even wanted to attach his own name to the new planet (his protector Arago argued him into suggesting that Uranus be called "Herschel"), but he was overruled and the planet became known as Neptune. Its major moon was discovered during the same year. That moon runs on an orbit tilted some 40 degrees against the orbit of the planet in retrograde fashion, but the rotation of the planet is normal, not retrograde, as was first believed.[1]

Then the watch was on Neptune's motion. Early in this century several astronomers (Crommelin, Grigull, Lowell, and others) became convinced that there had to be at least one more planet. Percival Lowell died in 1916, but his observatory continued the search. The planet was found by Clyde Tombaugh and the discovery was announced in 1930. The date of the announcement (though not of the discovery) was March 13, Lowell's birthday.

The new planet, which during the theoretical discussions had been generally referred to as "Trans-Neptune," was called Pluto. It was a surprise in every respect. Any astronomer who had been asked to speculate a bit about

[1] Ever since the discovery of Neptune's large moon it was more or less taken for granted that Neptune might have more, but too small to be visible to us. On the first of May, 1949, Dr. G. P. Kuiper, who also is the discoverer of Uranus' fifth satellite, got a picture of a tiny body which looked like another moon of Neptune, on a photographic plate with the aid of the 82-inch telescope of McDonald Observatory in Austin, Texas. But the case was still doubtful until more plates, taken on May 29, confirmed the discovery. The new moon is so far from its primary that it needs two terrestrial years for a revolution. Its diameter is of the order of 200 miles.

the "Trans-Neptune" prior to the actual discovery would have said that he expected it to be rather large, of the general order of size of Neptune. He would have added that it would be a low-density planet like the other four giants. As for its orbit, he would have expected it to move far outside the orbit of Neptune, as indicated by the provisional designation, say at least twice as far from the sun on the average as Uranus. He would have expected it to have moons, although they might not be visible from earth.

Pluto was found to have a highly eccentric orbit which did not lie far outside the orbit of Neptune by any means. In fact, Pluto's perihelion is even *inside* Neptune's orbit. And the planet itself is not a giant. In size it about corresponds to earth. It is strangely heavy and must be quite dark. Of course not much is known about it yet.

Since everything turned out to be different from expectations, it is not surprising that a few of the old guard which did the theorizing tend to feel that Pluto is not the ninth planet they had been looking for, but an unexpected and unsuspected extra member of the solar family. The real "Trans-Neptune" might still be undiscovered.

XXV. Surface of Mercury. The sun appears three times as large as we see it and since Mercury always points the same hemisphere to the sun, the temperature in the centre of that hemisphere must be about that of melting lead. Even though clad in asbestos suits, the explorers could not leave the protection of their ship for long. (Visual angle 40 degrees.)

I

XXVI. View from spaceship's cabin, sometime during 1985. Position: 11,000 miles beyond the orbit of the moon. Earth and moon appear as two sickles; the bright spot above the comet is Venus; the comet itself the most famous of all, Halley's comet, which approaches the sun four times in three centuries. The direction of the sun is indicated by the facts that comets' tails always point away from the sun, and that the light bulge of a planet naturally points in the direction of the sun.

122

XXVII. Venus as seen from a spaceship approaching the planet from inside the solar system, with the sun at its back. Seen from earth the planet appears as a featureless disc and this condition will probably continue to prevail even for spaceships until the ship gets fairly close, unless it is equipped with very powerful optical instruments. The "double star" at the upper right is the earth-moon system; if the picture were in colour the earth would look blue, the moon bright yellow.

123

XXVIII. Surface of Venus, which might be a dust bowl, with hazy and cloudy skies and wind-blown dust etching the rocks into fantastic shapes.

124

XXIX. Surface of Mars. Although it is considerably colder than earth and clothed in only a threadbare chilly atmosphere, the fourth planet still is provided with more earthlike features than any other. This is what an explorer would see if he were standing on the thin snowdrifts of the polar cap, looking towards the setting sun. (Checked for colour by Dr. Edison Pettit of Mount Wilson and Palomar Observatories.)

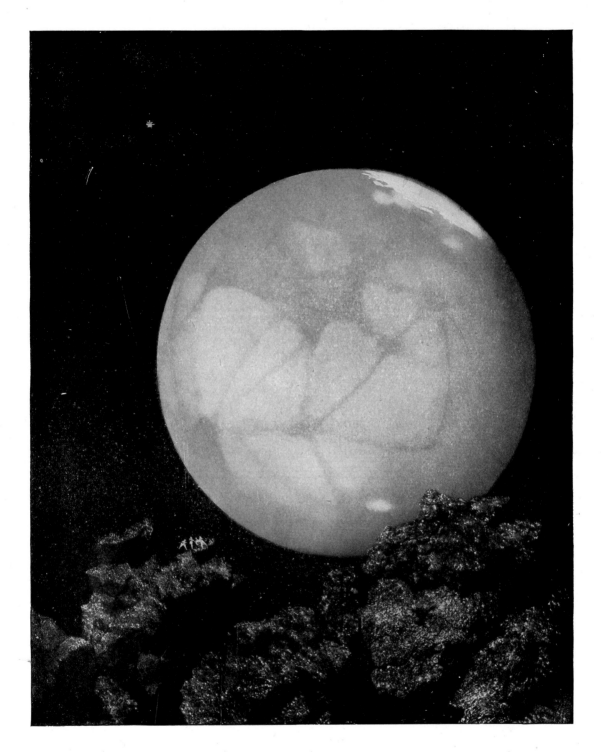

XXX. Mars seen from Deimos, its farther moon (visual angle 30 degrees). The black triangle near the centre is the *Syrtis major*, one of the first features seen by astronomers. The round spot in a larger circular light area is *Lacus solis*, the "Lake of the Sun." Brightest part of the picture is the south polar ice cap. (Checked for "canals" by Dr. Edison Pettit.)

XXXI*a*. Another view of Mars from its
farther moon Deimos (visual angle 40
degrees).

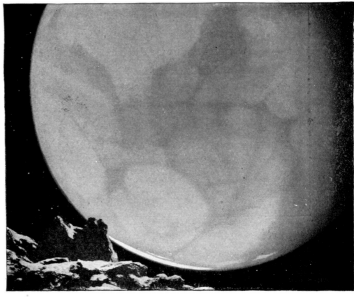

XXXI*b*. Mars as seen from Phobos, its
nearer moon (visual angle 40 degrees).

XXXII. Mars seen from Deimos. Again the polar cap and *Syrtis major* are the most prominent features. (Checked for colour and "canals" by Dr. Edison Pettit.)

128

XXXIII. Saturn as it appears in the dark sky of its satellite Japetus (visual angle 30 degrees). Japetus is about half the size of our own moon, but is 2,210,000 miles from its planet.

XXXIV*a*. Saturn seen from Phoebe, its outermost satellite, 8 million miles from the planet (visual angle 30 degrees). Its apparent size from there is about that of the moon seen from earth.

XXXIV*b*. Saturn as it appears from the surface of its satellite Rhea (visual angle 30 degrees). Four inner satellites are visible as are the edge and the shadow of the rings.

XXXV*a*. Saturn as it appears from its satellite Dione, 234,000 miles from its planet, or almost the same distance that our moon is from earth. Diameter of the satellite is 900 miles, less than half that of our moon.

XXXV*b*. The rings of Saturn seen from a position on the planet at $15\frac{1}{2}$ degrees northern latitude, corresponding to Guatemala. The black opening in the ring is known as Cassini's division.

XXXVI. Saturn as seen from its satellite Titan. Since Titan is large (3550 miles in diameter) and is known to have an atmosphere, the presence of water (frozen) was assumed. The sky would be blue, not black. Saturn is in ''new'' phase, 760,000 miles away from the satellite.

XXXVII. Saturn as seen from its small but near satellite Mimas, 115,000 miles from the planet (visual angle 30 degrees). As previous pictures also show, the rings, while wide, are surprisingly thin. When looked at "edge on" from earth, they disappear from view unless the observer has an exceptionally large and powerful instrument at his disposal. Although the rings, consisting as they do of cosmic debris, are tenuous in themselves, they produce a deep shadow. The spot under the ring shadow is the shadow of one of the satellites.

133

XXXVIII*a*. Uranus, seen from its third major satellite. Below the planet are other satellites, above the planet is the constellation Ursa Major (Big Dipper). Orbits of satellites are almost vertical to the plane of the ecliptic (82.2 degrees).

XXXVIII*b*. Neptune, seen from its major satellite, 220,000 miles from the planet, a little closer than our moon. But as compared to the prevailing direction in the solar system, Neptune's moon (unofficially called "Triton") moves backward in its orbit.

Chesley Bonestell ©

XXXIX. Pluto, the outermost planet of our solar system. Surprisingly, Pluto, unlike the other outer planets of our solar system, turned out to be small and massive. Its atmosphere must lie frozen on the rocks. From that distance the sun looks like a brilliant distant arc light, without perceptible disk.

135

XL. Close-up of another sun. The almost incredible system of the double star Mira, seen from
an imaginary (but possible) planet 450 million miles from the surface of Mira. The star itself
is a so-called "Red Giant," so tenuous that it does not even produce a well-defined boundary.
Its size is such that, if the sun were placed in its centre, the planet Mars would skip along the
uncertain surface. But the mass of Mira is probably only ten times the mass of the sun. Mira
undergoes very pronounced changes of luminosity in 330-day intervals; the picture shows the
darkest phase. Mira's star companion is a white star, probably somewhat smaller than our
sun and remarkably faint for a white star, a fact which delayed its discovery. In the picture it
is assumed to be 47 million miles from the planet, and is shown in transit across the gigantic
disc of Mira. (Detail of the painting checked by Doctors Alfred H. Joy and Robert S. Richardson of Mount Wilson and Palomar Observatories.)

4. "VERMIN OF THE SKIES"

IT WAS during the night preceding the first of January 1801. It was a clear night over Italy and the stars shone distant and cold from the wintry sky where the constellation of Orion stood high.

New Year's Eve is not often used for observations—astronomers usually spend it with their families. But Professor Giuseppe Piazzi, being a monk, had no family. After services he had gone to his observatory with a special purpose in mind. A recently published star catalogue contained a misprint. Conditions were fine for correcting this mistake. While working he discovered a small star of the sixth magnitude, just barely visible without telescope, in a place where no sixth-magnitude star was listed. In addition, it seemed to change position slowly.

Both these facts made it clear that it could not be a "star," that is, a distant sun, but had to be a member of the solar system. Professor Piazzi thought that he had discovered a new comet which was still far enough from the sun not to have developed a tail. He followed it for several nights, measuring its apparent positions so that the orbit might be calculated. The calculations was done by a young man who showed exceptional promise as a mathematician. His name was Karl Friedrich Gauss, and it is still the greatest name in mathematics. And Gauss, before he had progressed very far, realized that Piazzi had made a great discovery. The new "comet" did not have the elongated orbit typical of comets. In fact its orbit was more nearly circular than that of Mars or Mercury. And its average distance from the sun was 2.77 astronomical units, or 2.77 times as far as the distance of the earth from the sun.

There was something special about this very figure. When Kepler was still a young man, he believed, like all astronomers of his time, that the orbits of the planets were circles. He spent years wondering about the mathematical relationships between the radii of these circles. Finally he thought that he had found the answer: there were the "five regular solids" of geometry and the distances of the planets seemed to conform to an arrangement of these solids, one inside the other. But something failed to fit—the distance between Mars and Jupiter was much too large. It did not work out unless an additional planet was assumed there. He wrote simply: *Inter Jovem et Martem planetam interposui*—"Between Jupiter and Mars I put a planet."

His own discovery of the ellipticity of planetary orbits made his earlier scheme unnecessary and obsolete. But to all his successors it still looked as if there were an unreasonable "hole" between these two planets. And during the period between Kepler and Gauss an amusing rule had been devised. It consisted of taking 4, adding it to 3 or a multiple of 3, and dividing the result by 10. The final figure, if taken to mean astronomical units, agreed quite closely with the actual distances of the successive planets. But there was no planet for the value of 2.8 until Gauss showed that Piazzi had "put a planet between Jupiter and Mars." The new planet was named Ceres.

THE BODE-TITIUS RULE[1]

$4+(\ \ 0\cdot3)\,/\,10=\ \ \ 0.4;$	Mercury,	actual distance	0.39
$4+(\ \ 1\cdot3)\,/\,10=\ \ \ 0.7;$	Venus,	actual distance	0.72
$4+(\ \ 2\cdot3)\,/\,10=\ \ \ 1.0;$	Earth,	actual distance	1.00
$4+(\ \ 4\cdot3)\,/\,10=\ \ \ 1.6;$	Mars,	actual distance	1.52
$4+(\ \ 8\cdot3)\,/\,10=\ \ \ 2.8;$	Ceres,	actual distance	2.77
$4+(\ 16\cdot3)\,/\,10=\ \ \ 5.2;$	Jupiter,	actual distance	5.20
$4+(\ 32\cdot3)\,/\,10=\ 10.0;$	Saturn,	actual distance	9.54
$4+(\ 64\cdot3)\,/\,10=\ 19.6;$	Uranus,	actual distance	19.19
$4+(128\cdot3)\,/\,10=\ 38.8;$	Neptune,	actual distance	30.07
$4+(256\cdot3)\,/\,10=\ 77.2;$	Pluto,	actual distance	29.00–42.00
$4+(512\cdot3)\,/\,10=154.0;$	X		————

[1] It can be seen that everything works out nicely from Mercury up to and including Uranus. Neptune is badly off and Pluto even worse. Some enthusiastic believers in this rule have said that Pluto is not the expected "Trans-Neptune" for this reason alone. Whether there is a physical law hiding behind this rule is completely a matter of conjecture.

That the planet which at long last fitted into this space was so small—we now know that Ceres's diameter is about 480 miles—was somewhat surprising, but this at least explained why it had not been discovered earlier. But the real surprises were still ahead.

One year after Piazzi's discovery, a physician in Bremen, Heinrich Wilhelm Matthäus Olbers, M.D., who was an enthusiastic and well-reputed amateur astronomer, found another small planet near that much-discussed distance of 2.8 astronomical units. The date of the discovery is known—it was March 28, 1802. Doctor Olbers apparently had been comet-hunting, and the discovery of the second small planet was accidental. It was called Pallas and its diameter is now listed as 304 miles. In 1804 a third small planet was discovered—by Harding—and called Juno. Its diameter must be rather less than 200 miles. Three years later Dr. Olbers found a fourth and named it Vesta, and we now know that its diameter is of the order of 240 miles.

There was some surprise that four planets had been found where even an optimist had hoped for only one, but Dr. Olbers had an answer. He stated that there probably had been only one planet in the orbit originally and that it, for some unknown reason, had exploded to form Ceres, Pallas, Juno, and Vesta. This explanation, after lying dormant for half a century, now finds favour again with most astronomers, but a series of explosions is considered more likely than one big blow-up—we discuss this a little more later.

For some reason that has been forgotten, astronomers seem to have thought that there could be only four of these small planets. In about 1830 another amateur, M. Hencke of Driesen, began to hunt for a fifth and succeeded in finding it after 15 years of work. It was named Astraea. Hencke, encouraged, kept on and after another 2 years found number 6, Hebe.

Then others got busy. Number 7 was found: Iris. Then number 8: Flora. Then number 9: Metis. Number 10: Hygeia. Number 11: Parthenope. Number 12: Victoria. And number 13: Egeria. And, precisely half a century after the discovery of Ceres, number 14: Irene.

The time interval from 1850 to 1870 yielded an average of five new discoveries per year. For as long as possible the discoverers stuck doggedly to the tradition which had been started, all names were female and classical, or at least with a classical sound. (82)-Alkmene, (29)-Amphitrite, (129)-Antigone, (94)-Aurora, (43)-Ariadne, (202)-Chryseïs, (34)-Circe, (27)-Euterpe, (40)-

Harmonia, (108)-Hecuba, (69)-Hesperia, (85)-Io, (179)-Klytemnaestra, (35)-Leukothea, (18)-Melpomene, (57)-Mnemosyne, (55)-Pandora, (26)-Proserpina, (33)-Polyhymnia, (80)-Sappho, (30)-Urania. All the goddesses and nymphs the Classical Lexicon would yield, the nine muses, the *Odyssey* from (195)-Eurykleia to (53)-Kalypso, spelled with "k's" in precise transliteration of the Greek.

But by 1890, a total of three hundred were known and names were running short. (210)-Isabella was no longer strictly classical. Nor was (208)-Lacrimosa. (Just what was its discoverer thinking about?) And in that year Professor Max Wolf of Heidelberg adopted a suggestion made by Dr. Isaac Roberts. He used the photographic plate. Now the so-called "asteroids," or better planetoids, were no longer hunted down patiently, they were caught in a photographic net. If you follow the apparent movement of the fixed stars with a camera attached to the telescope the stars produce sharp images on the plate. But a planetoid moves during the hour-long exposure time and betrays its movement, and existence, by a short line (Fig. 15). The results were gratifying or terrifying, depending on the point of view. The Germans patiently established the *Rechen-Institut Kleine Planeten* (Computing Institute Minor Planets) into which the whole world fed its discoveries, observations, and suspicions. But they also talked despairingly of the *Kleine Planetenplage* (minor planet pest), while an American astronomer who kept this particular contribution to his science anonymous called the planetoids "vermin of the skies." He probably had a photographic plate, exposed for an entirely different purpose, "crawling" with short tracks.

Classical names had run out before the list had grown to the three hundred mark. Mythology in general had been called in to provide some: (165)-Loreley, (242)-Kriemhild, (373)-Melusina. Countries were honoured: (232)-Russia, (241)-Germania, (477)-Italia, (916)-America. Cities: (325)-Heidelbergia, (484)-Pittsburghia, (787)-Moskva (Russian form of "Moscow"). Colleges: (736)-Harvard, (1312)-Vassar. Districts: (1256)-Normannia, (715)-Transvaalia, (1279)-Uganda (used as a female name!). Honours were handed out: (1000)-Piazzia, (1001)-Gaussia, (1002)-Olbersia, plus at least fifty more recent astronomers, like (855)-Newcombia and (1334)-Lundmarka. There is even one for a famous Indian (or for the tree named after him), (1103)-Sequoia. And I think that (1010)-Marlene actually means Marlene Dietrich.

How tight things got can be seen by the following examples: (448)-Natalie, (1121)-Natasha (the later being the diminutive of the former), (680)-Genoveva, (1237)-Geneviève (German and French forms of the same name), (710)-Gertrud, (1267)-Geertruida, (1382)-Gerti (no comment), (949)-Hel, (699)-Hela, (101)-Helena, (522)-Helga, (1075)-Helina! As time went on they began to make up names: (443)-Photographica, (692)-Hippodamia (this one stumps me), (996)-Hilaritas, (1165)-Imprinetta, (1192)-Prisma, (1240)-Centenaria, and (1224)-Fantasia. Worst of the lot is probably (694)-Ekard which would stump me too if I did not know from Dr. Richardson that it is "Drake" (University) spelled backward! There also were some gentle hints for donations—(671)-Carnegia, (904)-Rockefellia—but one principle was always adhered to: all names, by hook, by crook, and by definition, were female.

The first fifteen or twenty planetoids had brought honour to their discoverers, the next fifty or so brought recognition, the next two hundred were still news. After that it was routine.

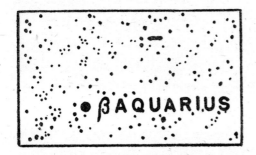

Fig. 15. Part of the photographic plate that led to the discovery of Eros. The telescope followed the stars, which therefore appear as points; the short line near the centre in the upper half was caused by the orbital movement of Eros.

But even in that field honours were still to be won. The next big event was a planetoid which was discovered photographically on August 13, 1898, by Dr. G. Witt of the Urania Observatory, Berlin. Doctor Witt saw at once that something exceptional had been caught in the light-sensitive dragnet. The line was unusually long, indicating high velocity. That, in turn, meant that this particular planetoid was unusually near. All observatories that could spare telescope time went after "1898 DQ" and soon after Dr. Berberich of the *Rechen-Institut* published a computation of the orbit. It has been improved since, but

141

not much. Then the planetoid was officially numbered (433) and given a name. The name was Eros.

The first masculine name, and for a good reason. Doctor Witt, to paraphrase Kepler, has put a planet between earth and Mars. The average distance of Eros from the sun is less than that of Mars, the length of its year is 643 days, and its perihelion is at 1.13 astronomical units, which means that it can approach earth within 14 million miles (the closest Mars can come is 34.6 million miles, and dark Venus 26 million miles). Closest approach takes place if Eros's 643 days and earth's $365\frac{1}{4}$ days work out in such a way that Eros passes its perihelion during the last week of January, any year. Unfortunately the closest possible approach took place in January 1894, four years before Eros was discovered. (A search of the plates at Harvard College Observatory revealed 17 accidental photographs of Eros taken during that approach.) An equally good approach will take place in January 1975. The best during that interval was in January 1931, when at about midnight January 30/31, the distance was 16.2 million miles.

Eros is interesting not only because of its orbit. Some observations have indicated that it might not even be spherical in shape. It is not too difficult to prove that a heavenly body must assume a spherical shape, provided it is large enough. With sufficient mass the gravitational stresses must overcome the strength of the material, so that, for example, a cube of the size of Mars is impossible. The corners which "stick out" would crumble and slide down the sides where they are nearer the centre. Of course the strength of the material does play a rôle to some extent: a cube of steel could still be a cube while the same mass of soft rock would already have been reduced to a sphere. Eros is estimated to be about 17 miles in diameter, and at that size a nonspherical shape is still possible.

The very next discovery, (434)-Hungaria, was also a planetoid unusually far inside the solar system, but since its average distance was more than that of Mars, (434) still received a female name. By that time it had already become clear that there are gaps in the ring of the planetoids, similar to the divisions of Saturn's rings and for the same reason of gravitational attraction. The disturbing element in this case was Jupiter (Fig. 16).

A few figures now become necessary. Expressed in astronomical units the

142

mean distance of Mars from the sun is 1.524 and that of Jupiter 5.203. The average motion of Jupiter on its orbit within 24 hours is almost precisely 300 seconds of arc. There are 60 seconds of arc in 1 minute of arc and 60 minutes in 1 degree; consequently Jupiter needs almost 12 years to describe the full circle of 360 degrees. The mean daily motion of Mars is 1887 seconds of arc (written 1887″). Eros, being on the average closer to the sun than Mars, has a mean daily motion of 2015″, but Eros is a special case. Hungaria, at 1.9 astronomical units' distance and with a mean daily motion of 1309″, represents the inner boundary of the "proper" (female) planetoids. The main swarm begins at about 2.1 astronomical units and 1100″ daily motion and extends to a distance of around 3.6 astronomical units with a little over 500″ mean daily motion. Still farther out, at 3.9 astronomical units, and with a mean daily motion of 449″ is a group of half a dozen planetoids called the Hilda Group (first discovered: (153)-Hilda), and at 4.3 astronomical units with a mean daily motion of 404″, planetoid (279) was found. It was taken to be the outermost planetoid and, with reference to the classical Ultima Thule, was named Thule.

All the time there hovered in the background the nagging question: why were there several hundred very small planets instead of one bigger one? As has been mentioned, Dr. Olbers had suggested that the four planetoids known in his time had been formed by the explosion of a single planet. The idea had been quietly accepted then, but gradually it became neglected. The main reason may have been that this hypothesis brought on the inevitable counterquestion of what had caused the original planet to explode. And that would have been a very hard question to answer, expecially in view of the fact that even the original planet must have been the smallest in the solar system— provided it had existed at all. Even now, when we know more than a thousand planetoids as compared to Olbers' four, the estimated total mass is anything but impressive. If they could all be gathered together they would make a planet far smaller than our moon.

But neglecting the explosion theory did not, of course, answer the question. And there existed, at least in theory, a possibility of deciding the fundamental issue. It should be possible to tell whether or not the planetoids were actually the remains of a larger planet. It they were, their orbits should show

143

a certain relationship: one should be able to tell whether they had all originated from the same orbit. But since each of the orbits had been changed and perturbed in a number of ways since "the event," such an investigation involved a staggering amount of work. It would have been bad even in Gauss' day, when there were only half a dozen orbits to disentangle. Later on the problem became too tedious even to tackle.

But then came indications that some of the planetoids seemed to be "fragments" even as to shape. It has been mentioned that (433)-Eros might not be spherical. Of course the planetoid is too small and also too far away for its irregular shape to be observed directly with a telescope stationed on the surface of the earth. But its regular changes in brightness are at least suspicious. Furthermore, (15)-Eunomia and (345)-Tercidina show similar short-term changes of brightness, the periods involved being only a few hours. And after the idea of planet explosion had been revived by H. J. Jeffreys, Professor K. Hirayama did undertake the job which must have occurred to many and which had been shunned by all: the task of studying all well-known planetoid orbits to find their undisturbed forms and their common origin, if any.

Professor Hirayama then announced that it could not have been a single explosion. He did not find one common origin, but five different ones for five so-called "families," each "family" being named after its brightest member. In particular, he named the (8)-Flora family at 2.2 astronomical units with 57 members, the (170)-Maria family at 2.5 astronomical units with 13 members, the (158)-Koronis family at 2.9 astronomical units with 15 members, the (221)-Eos family at 3.0 astronomical units with 23 members, and the (24)-Themis family at 3.1 astronomical units with 25 members. Professor Hirayama feels that each family was produced by a different explosion. This makes the whole problem somewhat more difficult, because those five exploding planets must have been even smaller than the hypothetical single planet would have been. And the smaller a planet, the harder it is to think of a reason for it to explode.

More recently it has been suggested that these explosions were not true explosions, but that the original planet, and afterwards its five, six, eight, or twelve biggest pieces, were broken up by the gravitational might of Jupiter. (Of course, one can also turn the argument around and say that Jupiter prevented a larger planet from forming.) That Jupiter wrought some havoc in the planetoid belt is known. There are "gaps" in the belt, probably not completely empty, but most sparsely populated.

Knowing that Jupiter's daily motion is 300″ one could have forecast that there should be a gap in the planetoid swarm at 600″ or about 3.3 astronomical

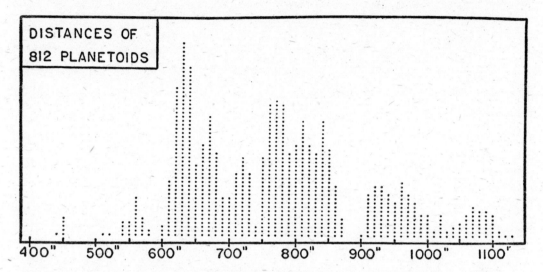

Fig. 16. The divisions of the ring of planetoids. The figures refer to the movement, in seconds of arc, during a 24-hour period. Jupiter's movement is almost precisely 300″ daily; we see "holes" at 600″ (twice Jupiter), 900″ (three times Jupiter), and even at 750″ (two and a half times Jupiter). Beyond 1100″ there are only a very few planetoids.

units, because the planetoids which presumably revolved there originally were too strongly influenced by Jupiter and thus thrown from their orbits. There is another gap at 900″ (three times Jupiter) and another one near 750″ (two and one-half times Jupiter). There is a faint one near 1050″ (three and one-half times Jupiter). Another faint gap can be found at 932″, caused by Mars, which moves twice as fast.

Most of this was already known—although with far fewer examples than we have now—when, on February 22, 1908, Professor Max Wolf discovered one more planetoid. Observations provisionally labelled "TG" were mailed to Dr. Berberich of the *Rechen-Institut* and he came up with the surprising news that here was a planetoid far beyond the main swarm, even beyond Thule. Presumably with some hesitation, Dr. Berberich announced that this (588) *seemed to move in the orbit of Jupiter!* This was, well, *unerhört* and hardly per-

145

missible. On top of that it was impossible. Even though (588), which was called Achilles, was rather massive for a planetoid—the diameter is now estimated to be of the order of 150 miles—it could not possibly hold out against Jupiter.

But Professor Charlier of Lund Observatory, looking at the orbit which Dr. Berberich and/or his hard-working assistants had computed, noticed that

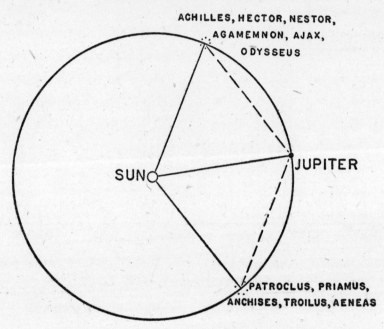

FIG. 17. "Jupiter Equilateral." About a dozen planetoids travel safely in the orbit of the giant; natural laws provide stability for a system in which the planetoids form equilateral triangles with Jupiter and the sun.

Achilles, apparently moving in Jupiter's orbit, was some 55½ degrees ahead of the giant. Figuratively speaking one might say that he yelped with surprise (maybe he did actually), because this—yes, this was a factual demonstration of a purely abstract mathematical concept. Way back in 1772 Joseph Louis Lagrange had written an essay on "Three Bodies" and what their mutual gravitational attraction would accomplish. Mostly his cases were examples of high instability, but there was one stable system. If three bodies formed an equilateral triangle, revolving in a circular or elliptical orbit around one of the three, the system would always remain an equilateral triangle, although it might change size during revolution if the orbit were elliptical. This was all

146

exceptionally fine mathematics but, of course, nothing else. It did not exist in reality—until Professor Charlier noticed that Achilles was almost 60 degrees ahead of Jupiter.

During the same year (617) was found, also in the orbit of Jupiter but this time 60 degrees behind. There was even a double equilateral triangle in space! (617) was named Patroclus. Then came (624) which proved to be close to Achilles. Since the reservoir of *male* classical names was almost untapped, astronomers took the *Iliad* off the shelf and named both groups after heroes of the Trojan War. It would have been nice if one group had consisted of Greek warriors only and the other of Trojans, but an early mistake ruined this. (624) became Hector, accompanied by (659)-Nestor and (911)-Agamemnon (Fig. 17). Like Achilles, all these planetoids are rather large, which probably means that the two groups contain numerous smaller members that cannot be detected from earth even photographically.

Even the heroes of the Trojan War do not represent "Ultima Thule." (944)-Hidalgo, discovered by Dr. Walter Baade at Bergedorf in 1920, has a "reasonable" perihelion distance of 2 astronomical units. Its aphelion, however, is at 9 astronomical units which is Saturn's orbit. Because of the enormous distance it travels, its period is 13.84 years.

Meanwhile more "males" were found this side of Mars' orbit and they not only command more interest but have even caused some fear. The first of them, after Eros, was discovered by Palisa in Vienna in 1911. It was (719)-Albert, a tiny body less than 3 miles in diameter which approached to within about 20 million miles of earth's orbit at perihelion but had its aphelion at 4.2 astronomical units, or about 90 million miles from Jupiter's orbit. Two others were found to have very similar orbits: namely, (887)-Alinda (something went wrong with the name), which also measures about 3 miles in diameter and was found by Max Wolf in 1918, and (1036)-Ganymede, with a diameter of about 20 miles, discovered by Baade in 1924. As for (719)-Albert, it has been lost, and one may speculate whether the visit to Jupiter's orbit proved unhealthy.

On March 13, 1932, Delporte in Uccle near Brussels sent out a report about the discovery of an "Object." This is a noncommittal term used when one is not sure whether one deals with a planetoid or with a tail-less comet.

147

Said "Object Delporte" came within 10 million miles 9 days after its discovery. It was a planetoid, (1221)-Amor. Astronomers had hardly recovered from their surprise when an "Object Reinmuth" was announced by Reinmuth of Heidelberg on April 24, 1932. Reinmuth, incidentally the discoverer of (911)-Agamemnon, felt quite sure that he had a planetoid and was correct. It was named Apollo and it came within 6.5 million miles. Its perihelion is just inside the earth's orbit and it is among the larger of the usually tiny male planetoids.

Astronomers were quite excited about this, because planetoids with their perihelions inside the earth's orbit might explain a few puzzles which are mentioned later. There was no danger, for the planetoid's orbit crossed that of earth not in the manner of two crossing streets but rather in the manner of a railroad bridge crossing a highway. Apollo was considered as "closest approach" as far as earth is concerned. But only until February 1936, when an announcement of another "Object Delporte" came from Brussels. It was Adonis, passing 1.3 million miles. And during the last days of October 1937, the excitement was increased some more by another "Object Reinmuth"— the planetoid Hermes passing on October 30 of that year at 485,000 miles. When the orbit was calculated—it is by no means really known—it turned out that those 485,000 miles had not been the closest possible distance. Hermes, 1 mile in diameter and with a mass of some 3 billion tons, can come as close as 220,000 miles, closer than our own moon.[1]

The orbits of all of these planetoids are long ellipses (Fig. 18) and except for the fact that they "do not lead anywhere" at either end they could be used in books on rockets as examples of spaceship orbits. They all have their perihelions inside the orbit of Venus; so far none is known that approaches the sun more closely than Mercury, but Adonis almost touches Mercury's orbit.

When the discoveries of several planetoids followed hard on one another's heels, some newspapermen got nervous and wrote scare stories of what would happen if one ran into the earth. Others, less easily frightened, came up with the question of whether the earth might not acquire a second moon in that manner. The latter question is the more easily answered: none of the known male planetoids could conceivably become a second moon of earth. When they

[1] No numbers are given for Apollo, Adonis, and Hermes, since numbering was discontinued "for the duration" at the outbreak of the war. The data on planetoids formerly collected by the *Rechen-Institut* are now being received by Dr. Paul Herget at the University of Cincinnati.

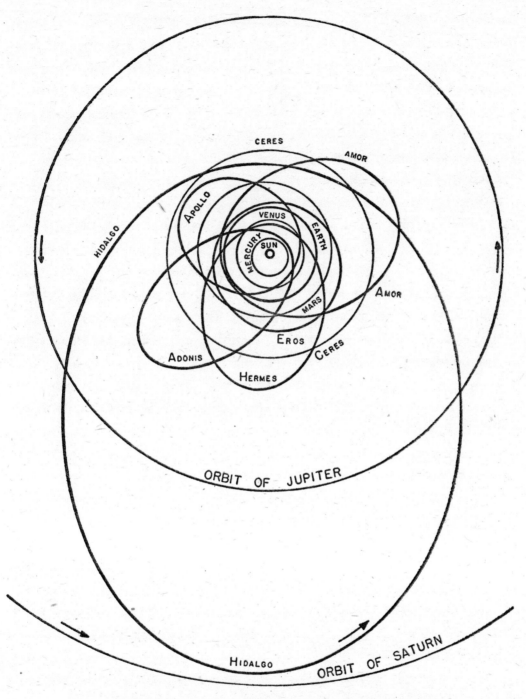

FIG. 18. The orbits of a number of "male" planetoids. That of Hermes is to be regarded as tentative, subject to later revision.

(Adapted from an illustration in *Astronomie*, by Lucien Rudaux and Gérard de Vaucouleurs, Paris: Larousse, 1948.)

pass earth's orbit they have velocities of 17 to 18 miles per second relative to our planet, being, as a rule, farther away than the moon. In order for them to be captured, their velocity, at that distance, would have to be less than $\frac{1}{3}$ mile per second. Of course, if one grazed our atmosphere it would lose much velocity, but in that case the alternatives are either that it would escape with a greatly changed orbit, or that it would enter the atmosphere again. In the latter case everything said about the landing manœuvre of a spaceship in the caption to Fig. 3 would apply to the planetoid: it would inevitably crash within a day or two after first grazing.

As regards the first question, about the direct impact of a planetoid, all that astronomers could say was that Hermes, Apollo, Adonis, and Amor had probably passed earth thousands of times before, that the orbits "crossed" only on a flat sheet of paper and not in three-dimensional space, and, finally, that three-fourths of the surface of our planet is water and more than half of the land is uninhabited. If one did strike in an inhabited area it would be a catastrophe for which there are no words. Even such a relatively small "object" as the one that caused the Arizona crater would cause destruction surpassing anything ever experienced. That "object" must have had a diameter of about $\frac{1}{4}$ mile. Falling on a city it would cause complete annihilation of an area over a mile in diameter, would completely devastate everything inside a circle some 12 miles in diameter, and cause damage of varying degrees of severity in an area up to 50 miles in diameter, measured from the point of impact.

But the chance that it will happen is infinitesimal.

It is unlikely that we already know all the planetoids with orbits like those of Hermes and others of his kind. Nor do we know whether there are others like Hidalgo.

We don't know either whether there are "Trojans" forming an "Earth Equilateral," a "Venus Equilateral" or even a "Moon Equilateral." So far nobody has looked for them, though that might be an interesting job for a gifted amateur with a reasonably large telescope. If there is a "Moon Equilateral" planetoid it might even have been photographed without being recognized—remember what happened to Eros. Since such a body would have to move as fast as the moon, its accidental trail on a plate would be so long that it would be taken for a meteor trail.

But Apollo may be the explanation for the mystery of "Vulcan" and the remarkable conversation which took place between the famous Leverrier and one Monsieur Lescarbault. Urbain Jean Joseph Leverrier, after having cleared up the cause of the perturbations of Uranus, decided to do the same with the difficulties presented by the orbit of Mercury. Assuming that these perturbations were caused by the existence of an "Intra-Mercury" he sat down and calculated where and how large this planet would have to be. When the calculation was finished Leverrier named his result "Vulcan." The problem then was to find it. Since it was, according to calculation, much closer to the sun than Mercury, it would be very difficult to see. Once the position was checked by observation one might find it more frequently, but the first discovery could probably be made only during an eclipse.

One day, in 1859, he received a letter, properly addressed to *Monsieur le Directeur de l'Observatoire*—a position which he had then held for 5 years. The sender was an amateur astronomer living some distance from Paris, Lescarbault by name. The letter stated that the sender had seen "Vulcan" in transit on March 26, 1859. Leverrier thought the letter important enough to make the journey to see Monsieur Lescarbault and to get what might be the last bit of information needed. Everybody who knew Leverrier in his later years described him as "opinionated" and "haughty." During that visit to Lescarbault both these attributes seem to have radiated at high intensity.

Monsieur Lescarbault, it turned out, was a small country doctor who earned additional and much-needed money as a cabinet maker and carpenter. Leverrier is said to have started the conversation with a severe reproach because Lescarbault had waited for several months after that transit before he wrote to the Observatory in Paris. Then he asked to see the telescope. Of course it was a cheap and small instrument but Lescarbault convinced Leverrier that he had seen a transit of Mercury with it. "Vulcan," Lescarbault said, had about half the diameter of Mercury—apparent diameter, of course—and his telescope would show a disk of such apparent size. Leverrier than asked to see the chronometer. Lescarbault had no chronometer, merely a big fat pocket watch of ancient vintage. He swore that this watch was very accurate. Leverrier pointed out that the watch had only hour and minute hands—how about seconds? Lescarbault triumphantly pointed at a chunk of lead suspended by a silk thread. This pendulum required precisely one second for a full swing. Leverrier could see that by looking at the length of the thread. Probably touched by the serious attitude of a poor man, Leverrier became more human at that point and asked whether Monsieur Lescarbault had tried to calculate the orbit of "Vulcan." Lescarbault replied meekly that he had tried it but did not get anywhere, since he was no mathematician.

Leverrier at least wanted to see the attempt and Lescarbault brought a few planed boards from his workshop. He explained that paper was dear. He therefore made his calculations on boards which he could plane off later. What Leverrier saw convinced him that Lescarbault was no mathematician. But it also convinced him that he was an honest man. And after his return to Paris he saw to it that Lescarbault was given the red ribbon of the *Légion d'honneur*.

After Leverrier had used the information obtained from Lescarbault to correct the orbit, professional astronomers began to hunt for "Vulcan," but without success. Max Wolf later compiled a list of nineteen observations of the period 1761 to 1865 which might have been "Vulcan," but of course it was impossible to check these old observations. The twentieth case furnished a clue to what some of the others may have been. A German by the name of Weber who lived in northeast China reported that he had seen a transit on April 4, 1875. By pure accident astronomers in Madrid had looked at the sun too on that day, but with a bigger instrument. And the bigger instrument had shown a small sunspot, approximately round. An announcement in 1878 also turned out to be a mistake.

Long after Leverrier's day the problem of Mercury's orbit was explained without need for an "Intra-Mercury." But what Lescarbault might have seen remained unexplained—until Apollo's orbit was computed. It may also have been one of the male planetoids which caused reports about a Venus satellite during the eighteenth century. Of course (assuming it to have been a planet-oid) the object was not seen actually "near" Venus. It was seen nearly in line with Venus.

And this ends the story of the planetoids for the present.

Inter Jovem et Martem planetam interposui. . . .

Yes, the third era will put many temporary "planets" into space. And not only between Jupiter and Mars.

XLI. The destructiveness of even a solid piece of non-explosive matter can far surpass that of the fission bomb—provided the solid piece is large enough and moves fast enough. This is what would happen if a very large meteorite (or very small planetoid) scored a hit on Manhattan. The meteorite was assumed to be of the same size as that which caused Meteor Crater in Arizona some 8,000 years ago. In addition to the direct destruction, the heat generated by passage through the air and by the impact would ignite all structures for miles around.

XLII. Martian landscape, with eroded mountains in distance, canal and dust storm, desert;
green areas and eroded hillside in foreground.

XLIII. Martian landscape, looking toward the pole across a frozen pond and desert areas. One of the dust storms which have been observed from earth is sweeping across the desert and the green areas which surround the polar ice cap. The green areas are almost certainly plant life, but the plants are probably of a type which can extract moisture from the atmosphere.

155

XLIV. Jupiter as seen from its large moon Europa, which is about 416,000 miles from the planet, or not quite twice as far away as our moon from us. The albedo (reflective power) of this moon is 20 per cent greater than that of the planet itself, indicating that it must be covered with frozen gases and ice.

156

XLV. Jupiter as it appears from the surface of its innermost satellite, which is called "Jupiter v" because it was the fifth satellite to be discovered. The four large ones were discovered by Galilei immediately after the invention of the telescope. The distance to Jupiter is only 112,600 miles. Spots on the planet are shadows of some of the large satellites. In the upper portion of the planet's disc the now rather faint "Red Spot" can be seen.

157

XLVI. Jupiter's surface. Hydrogen flames and "lava" pour out off top of cliff. Lake below is liquid ammonia; cliffs are lava and ice.

XLVII*a*. Saturn's rings seen from a spot at 15½ degrees southern latitude on the planet (visual angle 40 degrees). They are illuminated by light reflected from the surface. The brilliant edges were seen in 1907 by Barnard during an over-edge view which showed dark side fore-shortened.

XLVII*b*. Saturn's rings, seen from surface during a midsummer night at 40 degrees southern latitude, looking due south (visual angle 40 degrees). Upper portion of crêpe ring faintly visible. Planet's shadow has red-tinged edge due to refraction.

159

XLVIII. The 200-inch telescope, showing in place, but without protective steel flaps. If space travel is developed quickly, this may remain the largest telescope ever built on earth.